1X9 =

2X9 = 18

3X9 = 27

4X9 = 36

5X9 = 46

Seven-Minute
Stories
for Church
and Home

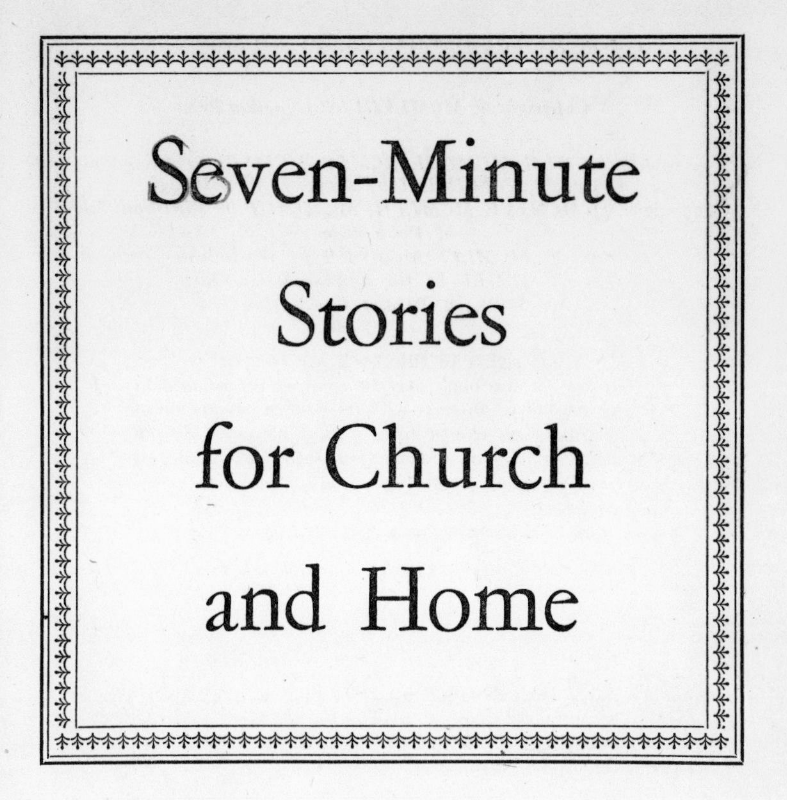

Seven-Minute Stories for Church and Home

ALICE GEER KELSEY

ABINGDON PRESS  NEW YORK • NASHVILLE

SEVEN-MINUTE STORIES FOR CHURCH AND HOME

Library of Congress Catalog Card Number: 58-5399

"The Possum's Tail," "The Race," "The Ball Game," and "The Kingfisher's Wish" are adapted from tales in *Myths of the Cherokee*, by James Mooney (in the *Nineteenth Annual Report of the Bureau of American Ethnology*, Washington: Govt. Printing Office, 1900).

Scripture quotations unless otherwise noted are from the Revised Standard Version of the Bible and are copyright 1946 and 1952 by the Division of Christian Education of the National Council of the Churches of Christ in the U. S. A.

Scripture quotations designated "Phillips" are from *Letters to Young Churches*, J. B. Phillips, 1950, used by permission of The Macmillan Co.

SET UP, PRINTED, AND BOUND BY THE PARTHENON PRESS, AT NASHVILLE, TENNESSEE, UNITED STATES OF AMERICA

Acknowledgments

THESE STORIES HAVE APPEARED IN PERIODICALS OR CURRICULUM. Appreciation is here expressed to the editors and publishers who have graciously permitted their reprinting or adaptation.

To the Disciples Christian Board of Publication for "Lito Finds His Talent," "The Other Half of the House," and "Each One Bring One" from *Junior World.*

To the Methodist Publishing House for "Go Down, Moses," "River Songs," and "The Beam in My Sister's Eye" from *Trails for Juniors.*

To the Philippine Federation of Christian Churches for "To Market" from *Stories for Children;* and "Timothy's 'Luck,' " "The Oil or the Book," "Lito Finds His Talent," "The Other Half of the House," "The Hidden Treasure," "Juan Tamad and the Lights," and "When the Bible Came Back" from *Your Church,* a vacation church school manual for juniors.

To the Pulpit Digest Publishing Company for "Have No Fear," "The New Law," "Many Sparrows," "Tongues of Fire," "The Good Shepherd," "Everyday Life," "Steal Away," "In-a My Heart," "A Refugee Gives Thanks," "Alone?" "Fun or Delight," "Ant-Watching," "Onesiphorus, a True Friend," "Diotrephes," "Two Boats," and "The Whole Armor of God" from *Pulpit Digest.*

To the Westminster Press for "The Eternal Flame of the Cherokees" from *Trailblazer;* and "The Tears of the Yunwi

Tsunsdi," "The Possum's Tail," "The Race," "The Ball Game," and "The Kingfisher's Wish" from *Stories.*

To the Sunday School Board of the Southern Baptist Convention for "The Boy Who Watched for Melchior" from *The Sentinel.*

Contents

STORIES OF NEGRO SPIRITUALS

STORIES FOR SPECIAL OCCASIONS

STORIES WITH TEXTS

WHEN OLD SCROLLS WERE NEW

These stories give boys and girls an idea why some of the New Testament books were written, how they were preserved and shared, and what they meant to those who heard the scrolls when they were new. The children of these stories are fictional but possible according to the most commonly accepted theories of biblical scholarship.

Have No Fear

(Introducing the Gospel of Mark)

RUFUS PEERED DOWN THE TWO NARROW ALLEYS. WHICH SHOULD he follow? Either would twist and turn to join the wide street that led through the gate into open country outside the walls of Rome.

He remembered the boys who lived in the alley that twisted off to the right. They had learned that his parents belonged to that little group called Christians who were despised and persecuted by most of the Romans in that long-ago time. If Rufus chose the road past the boys' house, they might dash out and make fun of him, "Christian! Christian! Rufus is a Christian!" They might even throw stones at him, or knock him down on the dirty cobblestones.

Rufus took a step down the other alley—then stopped. Ahead of him was the broad back of his neighbor Lucius the potter—a Christian so brave that he did not care who knew it. Lucius was in trouble most of the time for his boldness and his faith. His wife often sighed, "I never know whether he'll come home at night or be in prison waiting to be thrown to the lions."

Rufus did not dare walk through the streets of Rome with Lucius. It might be better to go home after all. It might be too dangerous to try to go to the catacombs where the Christians were meeting to read the new scroll written by Mark. But he did want to hear that scroll. Everyone who heard it had a new light in his eyes and new courage in his step. Rufus was tired of being afraid all the time.

Lucius was out of sight now. Rufus walked cautiously in the middle of the narrow road. He walked as far as possible from dark doorways from which some boy might dart with a taunting, "Christian! Christian! There goes a Christian!"

At last he reached the wide street. Here he could mingle in the crowds unseen. He ran through the gate onto the wide Appian Way that led on and on into far parts of the great Roman Empire. Rufus sometimes asked his parents, "Why don't the Christians leave Rome and travel to Macedonia or Palestine or Asia or any faraway place where we could be safe?"

But his parents always answered, "No place in the Roman Empire is safe for us. Christians are in danger everywhere."

Rufus turned from the Appian Way to follow a path toward an opening in the ground. He had gone into this catacomb once with his mother. He had been afraid to go again till today. Even the singing and prayers of the Christians could not take away the creepy, scary feeling of being in an underground cemetery. He wondered if there would be Roman soldiers barring the entrance when he wanted to leave.

"I hope the new scroll will be worth all this," Rufus thought. He entered the opening and followed the tunnel. It was dimly lighted by oil lamps set in niches hollowed out of the clay walls. He tried not to look at the rows of shelves cut on either side for the burial of the dead. The sound of singing led him on.

He found the Christians gathered in a wide underground room. His mother smiled at him. He wriggled his way among the people. She spread her cloak so that he could sit on it close to her.

The psalm was finished. Jason, a leader among the Christians, held the new scroll high so all could see it.

"This is the good news that you have come to hear," he said. "Mark knows how hard it is to be a Christian in these days of suffering and danger. On this scroll he has written for us the story of Jesus Christ who was never afraid. Mark has told us of the mighty works of Jesus. He has told us how we too can do mighty works if we have faith and courage."

"Read," said the people. "Read the good news from the new scroll."

Then Rufus listened. He watched Jason wind the scroll slowly from one stick to another as he read. Story followed story. Four fishermen leaving their nets and boats to follow Jesus. The healing of the sick. Preaching by the sea when simple words told great truths. A few loaves and fishes in the hands of Jesus making enough food for thousands of hungry people. Jesus in a storm—unafraid. Jesus telling his disciples how great their power would be if they prayed with faith. Jesus walking boldly toward Jerusalem where he knew his life was in danger. Jesus so great that not even the cross nor the tomb would keep him from those who loved him and believed in him. Jesus living again and telling his friends, "Have no fear."

The scroll was finished. Rufus and his mother started home together. The corridors of the catacomb did not seem creepy and scary. Rufus forgot that Roman soldiers might be guarding the opening. He was thinking of the words of Jesus to his disciples, "Take heart, it is I; have no fear."

Walking along the Appian Way and through the gate into the city, Rufus' mother said, "I must stop and see a friend. Will you wait?"

"Oh, I'll go on alone." And Rufus ran down the street.

He hesitated only a minute when he came to the first of the narrow alleys that twisted toward his own little house. It was the one that passed the boys who jeered, threw stones, or knocked him down on the dirty cobblestones. Within himself, Rufus could hear a strong, kind voice saying, "Take heart, it is I; have no fear."

Rufus turned up the alley with firm step. He marched boldly toward the boys playing in the street. His eyes smiled.

"Christian! Christian! Rufus is a Christian!" they taunted. The boys left their game and crowded around him. They clenched their fists and shook them in his face. "Christian! Christian! Rufus is a Christian!"

But Rufus surprised them. He did not run away. He did not cringe. He stood tall. He smiled and said, "Yes, I am a Christian. I'm proud of it!"

"Proud of it?" gasped the boys. "Why?"

"I'll tell you why," said Rufus.

And, remembering the good news of Mark's scroll, he told them why he was proud to be a Christian. The boys' hands were still clenched as they stood in front of him, staring as they listened. But Rufus did not care. There was a singing within him of a kind and powerful voice saying, "Take heart, it is I; have no fear."

The New Law

(Introducing the Gospel of Matthew)

THE BROOK FLOWING INTO THE MIGHTY ORONTES RIVER MADE a favorite play-spot for the Jewish boys of ancient Antioch. It was a good place to sail stick boats, or wade on hot days, or hunt little scurrying water creatures. Some days the boys took off their clothes for a good splash in the cool water.

This day they were playing on the bank of the little stream and keeping their tunics and sandals dry.

They had used up every game they knew. Suddenly Asa had an idea. Joram, who was larger than Asa, was standing at the edge of the brook. He was watching the play of lambs on the other side. His back was turned toward Asa. He was close to the edge and seeing nothing but the lambs' play. The smaller boy could not help wondering how big a push it would take to send Joram sprawling into the water. The more he wondered, the harder it was to resist trying.

With both hands and one knee, Asa pushed. Having no warning, Joram was thrown off balance. He toppled into the brook with a splash that was loud enough to satisfy any mischievous boy. Asa did not stand to watch the bigger boy climb out of the brook. He remembered that Joram could run faster and punch harder than he. Asa's sandals raised puffs of dust as he dashed across the fields toward home.

The other boys stood by. Watching Joram get even with Asa would be a good show.

Joram climbed out of the stream. He wrung the water from his tunic, shook it from his eyes and hair, and emptied it from his sandals. The boys stood aside to give him plenty of room when he started to chase Asa. They knew he could catch up with the smaller boy and trounce him well before he could reach the safety of his own house.

But Joram was not giving chase. Instead he did a strange thing. He stood at the edge of the brook, shaking himself dry, and laughing.

"Aren't you going to chase Asa?" asked Eliud.

"Aren't you going to beat him?" asked Rhesa.

"No," laughed Joram. Then he shouted, "Asa! Asa my friend! Don't run away. Come on back and throw me in the brook again!"

Asa heard, hestitated, but ran on. He was not going to be

tricked into going back. There was no telling what Joram would do to get even with him.

"Oh, I see your scheme," Eliud said to Joram. "You want him to come back so you can get even with him by tossing him in the brook!"

"Not that," answered Joram.

"But that's the law of Moses," said Rhesa. "It says to pay back when someone hurts you."

Eliud and Rhesa recited the law together, as they recited in the synagogue school: "Life for life, eye for eye, tooth for tooth, hand for hand, burn for burn, wound for wound, stripe for stripe" (Exod. 21:23-25).

"That is the *old* law," said Joram. "I learned that, too, when our family used to go to the synagogue. We are learning the *new* law now when we meet in Naaman's house evenings to hear the reading of the scroll."

"What scroll?" asked Eliud. "The scrolls of the law are in the synagogue. The rabbi reads them to us."

"Ours is a new scroll," said Joram. "We call it the good news according to Matthew. There are not many copies. We are lucky to have one for the church of Antioch."

"So that's what you Christians do when you meet in Naaman's house?" said Rhesa. "What does this new scroll of yours say about getting even when someone pushes you into a brook?"

"Come to Naaman's house with me," invited Joram. "We'll ask him to read that part to you."

On the long walk back to Antioch, the sun was hot enough to dry Joram's tunic. The mud on his sandals changed to dust. The boys went directly to Naaman's house, where they found the Christian sitting in front of a table copying the words of the new scroll onto a fresh piece of papyrus.

After the greetings were politely said, Joram asked, "Naaman, the boys want to hear what the new law says about getting even when anyone hurts you. They know the old law, and they wondered why I didn't follow it when Asa pushed me into the brook. Will you read that part of the new law to them?"

"Gladly!" Naaman put down his pen. He held the scroll in his right hand while, with his left, he rolled it on the sticks till he found the place he wanted.

Naaman began to read, "You have heard that it was said, 'An eye for an eye and a tooth for a tooth.' "

"We know that law," said Eliud, " '. . . hand for hand, burn for burn, wound for wound, stripe for stripe.' "

"That is the *old* law," said Naaman, "but listen to the new law, given by Jesus the Messiah." And Naaman began again to read, "You have heard that it was said, 'An eye for an eye and a tooth for a tooth.' But I say to you, Do not resist one who is evil. But if any one strikes you on the right cheek, turn to him the other also; and if any one would sue you and take your coat, let him have your cloak as well; and if any one forces you to go one mile, go with him two miles." (Matt. 5:38-41.)

The boys stared at Naaman. This was a hard law to understand.

"Will you read it again, Naaman?" asked Eliud.

"Gladly," said Naaman.

"But wait," suggested Rhesa. "Let's find Asa first, and bring him to listen. He'll be more fun to play with if he hears the new law too."

Many Sparrows

(Introducing the Gospel of Luke)

JULIA, THE LITTLE SLAVE GIRL, RAISED BOTH FISTS HIGH. THEY were tightly closed, holding something precious.

"Cheep-cheep," she called in the soft twittering voice she

saved for her friends, the little wild birds. "Come, my little sparrows, I have something for you. I found it on the ground near the mill where the men are grinding the wheat."

Julia opened her fists. Grains of wheat pattered on the tiled floor surrounding the cistern in the courtyard of her master's home. With a chirping and a whir of small wings, the birds fluttered from branches of palm and olive trees. Julia's voice was a contented murmur as she talked to the sparrows.

Sometimes, since her mother died, the little slave girl thought these birds were the best friends she had in the whole wide Roman Empire. Julia could not complain that anyone was unkind to her. It was that nobody really cared about her. Her master, Theophilus, was good to all his servants, but Julia doubted if he would recognize her if they happened to meet on the streets of their city beside the sea. Her mistress always smiled when Julia came running to open the gate for her, but it was only the smile of a great lady being gracious to a slave. The other servants were polite to Julia, so long as she was at her place each day to open the big street gate when anyone knocked. But there was nobody to whom it mattered that she was Julia. There were many, many slave girls who could open gates. That was why she felt a kinship to the little birds. There were many of them, too. And they did not matter to anyone either.

Before the birds had finished the wheat, there was a sharp knock on the gate. Julia jumped up so fast that the birds fluttered back to their perches in the trees of the courtyard. The girl opened the inner gate, then the outer gate that led into the street. A man stood there, holding a scroll in his hand. He seemed to be a traveler from afar.

"I have a scroll for Theophilus," said the man. "Is he here?"

"My master is in the garden." Julia spoke in her humble slave voice. "I will take you to him."

She latched the gate after the traveler and led the way through courtyard and corridor into the garden. Her master

Theophilus was sitting in the covered portico talking with friends.

"Most excellent Theophilus," the traveler greeted her master. "I bring you a scroll from the Greek doctor who used to travel with Paul."

"Ah, from Luke!" Theophilus welcomed the messenger, then turned to his friends. "Luke said he was writing the story of the Christians and of their Messiah, a carpenter named Jesus. This man was crucified but his followers believe he rose from the dead. I have heard something of the story and teachings, but I told Luke I would be interested to know more."

"This is the first scroll. It tells about Jesus," explained the traveler. "Luke is writing a second scroll. It will tell some of the acts of those who carried on Jesus' teachings. Luke will send you this second scroll when it is written."

As Theophilus opened the scroll, Julia sat quietly where nobody would notice her. She listened as Theophilus started to read.

You know the story of Jesus that Theophilus read from Luke's scroll. Try to imagine how it would sound to a little slave girl who felt lonely and unloved. You can guess which stories she liked best. Jesus taking the children in his arms to bless them. Jesus feeding thousands of hungry people. Jesus healing the servant of a captain.

You can guess which of Jesus' sayings she liked best. "Blessed are you poor, for yours is the kingdom of God." "Blessed are you that weep now, for you shall laugh." Or the story Jesus told about the Samaritan who was a good neighbor to a man who was hurt and alone.

But can you guess which of Jesus' words made such a glad song in her heart that she could repeat them without a mistake long after she went back to the courtyard to listen for more knocks on the big street gate? "Are not five sparrows sold for two pennies? And not one of them is forgotten before

God. Why, even the hairs of your head are all numbered. Fear not; you are of more value than many sparrows."

On her way back, Julia stopped in the kitchen to ask a crust of dry bread. In the courtyard she crumbled it and tossed it on the tiled floor, calling "Cheep-cheep" in the twittering voice she saved for the birds. As they ate, she had new stories to tell them.

"You thought I was the only one who cared for you," she murmured contentedly. "But I'm not. There's a loving God who cares for you, too. He may not keep you out of all trouble, but he loves you so much that he's sorry when anything happens to you. And . . ." Julia paused because what she was going to say was so important. She wanted to be sure the sparrows heard. "This same loving God cares what happens to *me*. He loves me just as much as though I were rich, and important and free. Every single person matters to God, even a little slave girl."

Tongues of Fire

(Introducing the Book of Acts)

YEARS HAD GONE BY. JULIA WAS NO LONGER A LITTLE SLAVE GIRL. She was a tall girl now, almost a young woman. She was walking through the narrow streets of her city by the sea on her way to the market place to buy food for the household of Theophilus. She had friends in many booths.

"It's good to see your smiling face," said the old woman who sold grapes. "You used to be a sad-faced little thing, but now there's such sunshine in you that it makes an old woman like me feel warmed."

Julia bought the grapes, smiled her thanks, and tried to speak. She wanted to tell the old woman how the good news in Luke's scroll had changed her from "a sad-faced little thing" to a happy girl. But suppose the old woman did not understand! She might even laugh! And a crowd might gather to listen! Julia walked on.

"Good morning to you," was the welcome of the crippled man who sold fish. "You look as though you had good news."

"I do have good news," said Julia, choosing fish from his basket.

"It's many a day since any good news came my way." The man sighed as he took the money from her hand. "I wish you had good news for me."

"Oh, I do!" Julia stood for a minute wondering how she could explain to him what Luke had written in the scroll. Just then a noisy woman began scolding about the high price of fish. Julia slipped away, glad she had been interrupted. After all, she did not have the right words to tell the cripple the good news in Luke's scroll. He might laugh at her if she said that a carpenter that lived in Palestine fifty or so years ago could make him happy.

On her way to the baker's shop Julia passed a blind beggar boy, droning, "I have no father, no mother. I have only you to help me."

Julia dropped a coin in his hand. She stood beside him, hunting for the words to tell him that the God who cares for sparrows cares for slave girls and blind beggars also. But the beggar boy groped his open hand toward another passer-by, droning, "I have only you to help me." Julia had waited too long.

Julia bought the bread and turned toward Theophilus' house. She felt shame that once again she had failed to share the good news that brought her comfort and joy. In return for the cloth bag full of purchases, the cook gave her a crust of old bread for her birds. She carried it to the courtyard to crumble for her friends, the sparrows.

"I can help God take care of you," Julia told them. "Why can't I help God show other people that he cares for them so much that he sent Jesus to tell of his love? I wanted to tell the old woman the good news—and the crippled man—and the blind beggar boy—and all the people in the market place. But I can't find the way to tell them why I am happy."

Just then there came a knock on the door. Julia scattered the last crumbs on the ground and ran to lift the latch.

"Oh, you are welcome to the house of Theophilus," she said when she saw who stood in the street. It was the same messenger who had brought Luke's scroll telling about Jesus. "Come in, sir."

"I have another scroll for the most excellent Theophilus," said the messenger. "Is he within?"

"He is in the garden. Follow me." Julia led him to her master.

"Luke has sent you the second scroll," the messenger explained to Theophilus. "It tells some of the acts of those who follow the Way of Jesus. It tells the brave deeds of Peter, Barnabas, Paul, and others."

"Call everyone of the household," Theophilus told Julia. "We will read the new scroll together."

So, sitting on the ground before Theophilus, Julia heard every word of the new scroll. It told how the disciples of Jesus had carried on his work after they were convinced that he was alive and was working through them. Near the beginning there was a strange story that was hard for Julia to understand—but very wonderful:

> When the day of Pentecost had come, they were all together in one place. And suddenly a sound came from heaven like the rush of a mighty wind, and it filled all the house where they were sitting. And there appeared to them tongues as of fire, distributed and resting on each one of them. And they were all filled with the Holy Spirit and began to speak in other tongues, as the Spirit gave them utterance. (Acts 2:1-4.)

Luke used the new words "Holy Spirit" many times in the scroll. Whenever one of the disciples was in need of help to do or to say the right thing, he could pray and feel the Holy Spirit bringing comfort and wisdom. As Julia listened to the reading, she learned that the Holy Spirit came to humble people, not only to great men like Paul or Peter. She learned that the Holy Spirit came to anyone who opened his mind in prayer and asked God for help. The Holy Spirit could come even to her!

Can you guess what happened the next time Julia walked through the market place? When the old woman who sold grapes asked why Julia was so happy, the girl told her about Jesus who came to earth to show God's love for everyone. When the crippled man who sold fish said he wished he could hear some good news once in a while, Julia shared with him the best news of all, that God would send his Holy Spirit to comfort the poorest of men. And when the blind beggar boy whined that he had no one to care for him, Julia sat on the ground beside the boy and told him about God who cares what happens to sparrows, and slave girls, and blind beggars.

The Good Shepherd

(Introducing the Gospel of John)

ESA TRUDGED BEHIND HIS TALL FATHER, NATHAN THE SHEPHERD. They did not come into the city often, so Esa tried to look in all directions at once. He and his father were stooping under loads of freshly carded wool they were bringing to market. Esa wished they could stop at some shops, but he knew he must follow his father directly to the wool market.

In the wool-buyers' street, they found their favorite wool merchant in hot discussion with some customers and neighboring merchants. Esa could not understand all they were saying but he knew they were arguing about religion. It was all very confusing.

One man was saying, "Moses is the greatest leader. He gave the Law which all Jews must follow."

Another was waving his hands and saying, "The Greek philosophers have all wisdom."

A third said, "I belong to the sect of John the Baptist. Even though he was beheaded by Herod many years ago, I believe his teachings of repentance and baptism are the greatest ever known."

Another said, "I belong to the group that follow Jesus of Nazareth, but not in the simple way that the early Christians followed him. We Christians have thought and argued about Jesus and his teachings till we have many new ideas to add to the old beliefs."

At that an old graybeard leaned heavily on his cane and said in a cracked voice, "I remember seeing this Jesus you talk about. I was just a tiny child in Jerusalem. It was at the time of the Passover. There was great shouting and cheering. I didn't know what it was all about, but of course I joined in the cheering. Children were waving palm branches before a young man who was riding through the gates of Jerusalem on a white donkey. I grabbed a palm branch and waved it in front of him too. I joined in the children's song:

> Hosanna to the Son of David!
> Blessed be he who comes in the name of the Lord!

Then the man on the donkey smiled at me, and I've never forgotten his face. I heard afterward that he was Jesus of Nazareth. I'm not a scholar and I can't argue with learned men. But I'm with anyone who believes in Jesus. I know his story has been written in scrolls."

"In three scrolls—of Mark, Luke, and Matthew," agreed the wool merchant. "When I was a young man, I thought I understood those scrolls. They seemed simple and true. But

I've heard too much learned talk about them since then. I don't know what to think. I wish someone would write a new scroll to answer all these new ideas."

"My friends," said a quiet voice that had not joined in the arguing. "There is a new scroll. It is written by an old man. He has lived so long that he had the story from Jesus' disciples. Also he has lived long enough to hear all the arguments about the three scrolls that tell of Jesus."

"Where is the new scroll?" asked the wool merchant.

"There are only a few copies of it," answered the quiet voice. "One is in our own city, at the house of Quintus."

"That's where the Christians meet to talk and pray together," said the wool merchant.

"Yes," agreed the quiet man. "Now they meet each evening to read this new scroll."

While the wool was being weighed, Nathan asked the way to Quintus' house. Esa was glad. He had liked the story told by the old man who remembered waving a palm branch before a young man on a donkey in Jerusalem. He would like to hear who this Jesus really was.

Nathan and Esa found Quintus sitting at a low table copying the words from a scroll onto a piece of papyrus.

"These are wonderful words I am copying." Quintus looked up as he welcomed his visitors. "The friends who meet here for prayer do not wish to spare this scroll, but they feel the Christians of other cities must have copies."

"What is the scroll?" asked Nathan.

"It is Jesus' story written by an old, old man named John. He has heard the arguments of many men about who Jesus really was. He has heard men read into the scrolls of Mark and Luke and Matthew things which are not there. And so John has written again the story of Jesus. He has written it to answer the questions of those who listen to the Greek philosophers, or those who love the Jewish law, or those who say John the Baptist is greater than Jesus. Anyone who reads this new scroll knows that Jesus is the Christ, the Son of God, who brings life to all who believe."

"Will you read to us from the scroll?" begged Nathan.

"Come any evening and hear it read," invited Quintus. Then he saw the disappointment in Esa's face, and added, "I'll read you one part that tells what Jesus is like. It is something this small shepherd boy will enjoy. Hear how Jesus describes himself."

Quintus rolled his scroll till he found the verses he wanted:

> I am the good shepherd. The good shepherd lays down his life for the sheep. He who is a hireling and not a shepherd, whose own the sheep are not, sees the wolf coming and leaves the sheep and flees; and the wolf snatches them and scatters them. He flees because he is a hireling and cares nothing for the sheep. I am the good shepherd; I know my own and my own know me, as the Father knows me and I know the Father, and I lay down my life for the sheep. And I have other sheep that are not of this fold; I must bring them also, and they will heed my voice. So there shall be one flock, one shepherd. (John 10:11-16.)

Esa knew how the poor timid sheep depended on their shepherd. He began to understand about Jesus.

Everyday Life

(Introducing the Letter to the Philippians)

News of Epaphroditus' coming had run ahead of him. A Roman traveling on horseback along the Egnatian highway brought the word.

"A ship from Rome docked at Neapolis this morning with one of your Philippian citizens aboard," said the Roman as he stopped for food in the market place of Philippi. "His name is Epaphroditus. He is coming on foot. I passed him on the road."

"Epaphroditus is coming!" The word spread from house to house where the Christians lived who were friends of Epaphroditus.

By the time the grownups had left their homes to walk out the Egnatian Road to meet him, some of the boys were already clipping fast along the paving stones toward Neapolis. Though he had been gone for months, these boys remembered him well —his kindness and his friendliness.

"Epaphroditus is coming!" the boys chanted as they ran toward him.

"He'll want to know everything that has happened since he went away to take our gift to Paul," said Erastus. "We can tell him how we go regularly to the church that meets in Lydia's house, and how we have been learning to sing psalms, and how we are giving more money in case Paul should need it again. He'll be glad to hear all that."

"You said he would want to know *everything,* Erastus," teased one of the boys. "Are you going to tell him *everything* you have been doing?" The other boys joined to tease Erastus with questions.

"Are you going to tell Epaphroditus how you fought with your brother and knocked out one of his teeth?"

"Or how you muddied the river on purpose when the women were washing clothes in it?"

"And then lied that a goat fell into the stream and thrashed around to make it muddy?"

"Or how you took money out of the bowl of the blind beggar?"

"And then bought sweets with the money and ate them all yourself?"

"Stop talking nonsense!" Erastus threatened them with clinched fists. "Epaphroditus doesn't care about things like that. He's interested in teaching the gospel Paul brought us, and in helping the church that meets in Lydia's house." Then they ran on to meet their friend.

Because Erastus' fists were strong, the other boys let him take the lead in telling Epaphroditus what had been going on in Philippi while he had been away. It sounded good as Erastus told it. Erastus made himself sound best of all.

"Good, my boys!" Epaphroditus smiled proudly at them. "I am glad you have worked so hard to be followers of Jesus' Way. The gospel will spread through all of Macedonia if the church has boys like you."

That evening the boys sat cross-legged in the front of the circle gathered about Epaphroditus. He had a special smile for them and a word of praise because they had been such fine boys. Erastus smiled in answer as though he deserved the biggest part of the praise. Then Epaphroditus unrolled a scroll to read the letter Paul had written and sent by him to the friends at Philippi.

"I thank God for you Christians at Philippi whenever I think of you," the letter began. It went on to tell how Paul longed to see them. It told how he had fared as a prisoner in Rome. Then the letter said something that made Erastus uncomfortable.

"But whatever happens, make sure that your everyday life is worthy of the Gospel of Christ." (Phil. 1:27 Phillips.)

Erastus squirmed a little. He squirmed more as the letter went on. Paul seemed to have written especially to a boy who thought that going to church, learning the psalms, and giving money would make up for fighting, stealing, lying, or teasing:

> Live together in harmony, live together in love. . . . Never act from motives of rivalry or personal vanity, but in humility think more of each other than you do of yourselves. . . . None of you should think only of his own affairs, but should learn to see things from other people's point of view. . . . Do all you have to do without grumbling or arguing, so that you may be God's children, blameless, sincere and wholesome, living in a warped and diseased world, and shining there like lights in a dark place. . . . Fix your minds on the things

which are holy and right and pure and beautiful and good. (Phil. 2:2-4, 14-15; 4:8 Phillips.)

Paul's letter went on to thank the Philippians for the money they had sent him by Epaphroditus. But Erastus was not listening to that. He was thinking of the number of times he had not lived up to Paul's rule: "Whatever happens, make sure that your everyday life is worthy of the Gospel of Christ."

Timothy's "Luck"

(Introducing the Epistles to the Ephesians, the Colossians, and Timothy)

THE SANDALS OF PHOEBE AND LINUS CLICKED ON THE WHITE pavement as they ran down the broad marble highway that led from their city of Ephesus to the Aegean Sea. They stopped every few minutes to look in the shops that lined the colonnades on either side of the street. They did not remind each other of their mother's warning, "Hurry to the fish market. Do not stop along the way to play or stare."

If either child had spoken of their mother's order, the other would have said, "But Mother will never know."

When Phoebe and Linus reached the waterfront, there were still more interesting things to make them forget their mother's, "Hurry to the fish market. Do not stop along the way to play or stare." They always loved to watch the boats come in—the little fishing boats and the bigger ships that came from afar. These big ships brought strange cargo and strange travelers.

At last the children reached the fish market which sprawled beside wharves where boats landed. They chose fresh fish from deep baskets. They bargained for the price as they had seen their mother bargain. They turned away, their money spent but their flat basket full of cool, moist fish. They stood on the wharf where a ship from afar was moored.

"I think it sailed from Rome," Linus said.

"See the two men coming ashore," Phoebe whispered to her brother. "I like their faces."

As the children watched, the two travelers picked up their bundles and started to walk the wide marble highway leading from the sea to the city of Ephesus. Other men came from the ship, but the children were interested only in the two men with the kind faces. Without realizing what they were doing, Phoebe and Linus were running beside them. Soon the men asked questions—the children's ages, their names, how far they must carry the fish. The children were telling more than they meant to tell, even about their playing on the way when their mother had told them to hurry.

"My name is Tychicus," the older man introduced himself. He put his hand on the shoulder of the younger man. "This is my friend Onesimus. We come from Paul, a prisoner at Rome. We bring a letter from him and from the church at Rome. It is for all the churches of Asia."

The children stared at Tychicus. They remembered Paul's visit to Ephesus, the visit from which their church had grown.

"Can you show us the home of a Christian?" Tychicus asked.

"We are Christians," the children answered together.

"Come to our house," invited Phoebe. "Mother will give you food and water. You can rest."

"While you rest, we will run to the houses of Christians," said Linus. "We'll tell them about the letter from Paul."

They turned down a small side street to their house. Their mother greeted them. In welcoming the travelers, she forgot to ask the children why they had been so slow. She hurried to the kitchen for bread and figs. She sent Linus to the fountain for a jar of fresh water. She led her guests to a cool spot under the grapevine by the door to rest.

The travelers were soon talking with Christians who hurried there as Phoebe and Linus spread the news. Those who could write agreed to do their share of copying Paul's letter for the other six churches of Asia. All agreed to come to their meeting place that evening to hear Tychicus read the letter from Paul.

"We hope you can stay with us many weeks," urged the mother of Phoebe and Linus.

"We would like to stay," answered Tychicus, "but we must travel soon to Colossae. We have two letters for that city—one for the church and one for a good man named Philemon. It is a long journey from Ephesus to Colossae, at least one hundred miles."

"Yes, I *know* it is a long journey," agreed Onesimus.

"Have you been to Colossae before?" asked Linus.

"Did not Tychicus tell you who I am?" asked Onesimus.

"He said you are his friend," said Phoebe.

"Now I am his friend," said Onesimus. He spoke slowly, as though the next words would be hard to say. "When I was in Colossae, I was the slave of the good Philemon. He was kind to me, but I wanted to be free. I ran away to the sea. There I found work on a ship going to Rome."

"But you were free in Rome," said Linus. "Why didn't you stay there? Why are you going back to Colossae to be a slave again?"

"In Rome I became a Christian," said Onesimus. "I was a friend of Paul and his helper Timothy and the other Christians of the church at Rome. I learned that a Christian is loyal and obedient. Then I knew I must go back to my master Philemon. Paul and Timothy wrote a letter for me to carry."

"Timothy?" asked the father of Phoebe and Linus. "Timothy? That was the name of the young man who was here in Ephesus with Paul. He was not much more than a boy, but he seemed to be of great help to Paul and the other Christian teachers. I wonder if it could be that same Timothy."

"It is the same," said Tychicus. "He helped Paul then. He helps more as he grows older. Paul trusts him to do many things. Timothy helps Paul with his letter writing. He goes on missions to churches. He was one of the seven men who carried the money from churches of Macedonia to the churches of Asia. Paul likes to have Timothy travel with him, and he sends him places where he cannot go himself. I do not know what Paul would do without Timothy."

"It is wonderful that anyone so young can do such work for the church," said the father of Linus and Phoebe.

"It is easy to understand," said Tychicus.

Phoebe and Linus saw the story look in Tychicus' eye. "Tell us!"

"Timothy had a good start, like you two children," said Tychicus. "He grew up in a home where the word of God was studied. His father was a Greek but he let his Jewish wife Eunice study the holy books of her people. Timothy's mother Eunice and his grandmother Lois took him to worship at the synagogue. At home they taught him the laws, the prophets, the history, and the poetry of the Jewish people. Paul often talks to Timothy about his good mother and grandmother. They were faithful to their Jewish beliefs till Paul and Barnabas visited the home town, Lystra. Then they believed Jesus' teachings and were even more faithful to the religion of Jesus Christ. And Timothy learned from them.

"On Paul's third visit to Lystra, he was needing a helper. He liked Timothy and he liked what the other Christians said about him. So Paul invited Timothy to travel with him."

"I wish I could be lucky like that," sighed Linus.

"It was not all luck," said Tychicus. He looked as though he wanted to explain how Linus and Pheobe would have to change if they expected to have the sort of "luck" that came to Timothy. But all he said was, "Listen to the letter when I read it tonight. There are a few words in it that explain why Timothy grew up to be the sort of young man that Paul could use."

That night while the letter was being read, Phoebe and Linus listened very hard. It was a long letter full of words they did not understand very well. But once Tychicus seemed to be looking straight at them while he read. The words he was reading were short and plain. Phoebe and Linus could understand them perfectly:

> Children, obey your parents in the Lord, for this is right. "Honor your father and mother" (this is the first commandment with a promise), "that it may be well with you and that you may live long on the earth." Fathers, do not provoke your children to anger, but bring them up in the discipline and instruction of the Lord. (Eph. 6:1-4.)

Tychicus did not need to tell Phoebe and Linus that the boy Timothy had learned to obey his parents in little things —like hurrying to market—as well as in big things.

STORIES OF THE CHEROKEE INDIANS

Those who know the reading tastes of American boys and girls say with regret, "It is hard to sell a book about *good* Indians." These stories introduce Indians whose goodness shows in their actions. It shows also in their folklore in which the kind or honest animals fare better than the proud and tricky.

The Eternal Flame of the Cherokees

A FLAME MORE THAN A CENTURY OLD—NOBODY KNOWS HOW much older—burns high in the Qualla Reservation up a winding road from the Indian village. If the Cherokee Indians have their way, this flame will burn forever. The inscription over the case that shelters this fire calls it "The Eternal Flame." The fire might be called "The Flame of Forgiveness." Its story is the story of a great act of forgiving on the part of the Cherokees who live in the Great Smokies.

Before you read the sentences engraved over the flame, listen to the story behind that inscription.

When white men first came to America, the Cherokee Indians all lived in the East. These Cherokees were peace-loving farmers who were ready to be friends with the pale-faced newcomers. The white explorers, traders, and settlers, however, did not bother to return the Cherokees' offers of friendship. Whether these white men came from Spain, France, or England, they failed to realize that the red men had rights to the land where their ancestors had raised their crops and hunted their game for as long as Indian legends stretched back and back through the years.

Even when the colonists formed the United States of America and declared that "all men are created equal," they did not treat the red men as free or equal. Though the Cherokees were crowded into smaller and smaller territory, they tried to remain friends with the white men who were pushing them. When General Jackson was hard-pressed by the Creek Indians (1814), it was the Cherokee warriors who fought on his side and brought him victory. It was a Cherokee chief, Junaluska, who saved the white general's life when a Creek attacked with a knife. In gratitude General Jackson told Chief Junaluska, "As long as the sun shines and the grass grows, there shall be friendship between us, and the feet of the Cherokee shall be toward the East."

But gratitude could not hold out against greed for gold. A yellow stone was found by an Indian boy playing by a brook. The news of that yellow stone started the rumor that there was gold in the Great Smoky Mountains. As the rumor spread, the Cherokees were pushed into smaller and smaller quarters. Finally, in 1838, General Jackson, who had become President Jackson, forgot his promise to Chief Junaluska, "As long as the sun shines and the grass grows, there shall be friendship between us, and the feet of the Cherokee shall be toward the East." President Jackson gave his consent to the plan to force all the Cherokees to move from their beloved mountain homes by the rushing Oconaluftee River. He agreed that they should migrate west to unknown wilderness in what is now Oklahoma.

The Cherokees, loyal to their home hills, resisted. But the United States Army was stronger than the Indians. Eleven hundred of the Cherokees, knowing their hills better than did the white men, hid in the highest peaks and ridges.

The rest of the tribe was sent on the long and grueling march.

Before they left their mountain home, the ones who were driven west gathered into fern-lined shells, some burning charcoal from their council fire. This was fire that had been kept alive for as many years as their oldest tribesmen could remember. The Cherokees resolved to keep it burning by taking it with them. Men, women, and children died of weariness, hunger, thirst, and exposure on that six-month trek, but the fire was kept alive. It was one thing from home —a sacred thing—to give the Cherokees courage in their new settlement in the wilderness so far from the hills they loved.

The other Cherokees, the 1100 who hid in the Great Smoky Mountains, could not keep their council fire burning when they fled to the caves and the high ridges. But they kept their courage burning. By 1951, 112 years after their tribesmen were driven west, these 1100 had grown to a tribe of 3500. Like the hills where they lived, these Cherokees were a rugged people. They had made their peace with the white men whose ancestors had abused them. They had won the respect of the white men. They went to schools the white men gave them, and to the churches the white men helped them build. They took advice from the agricultural agents and crafts teachers sent them by the white men's government.

But they earned their living by their own work. They were farmers, woodsmen, craftworkers, teachers, merchants. Because their village, Cherokee, in North Carolina, was on a much-traveled route, many could earn a living caring for the tourists who stopped at their motels, restaurants, or craft shops. The Cherokees started a museum full of Indian objects. They built a village to show the old Indian ways of life. Every summer they act a drama, *Unto These Hills,* in the mountainside theater to tell the story of the Cherokee Indians who stayed in the Great Smoky Mountains.

Remembering their story, even though they had made friends with the white men who brought it about, the East

Band of the Cherokees in 1951 sent four of their leaders to Oklahoma to visit the members of their tribe whose ancestors went on the "trail of heartbreak" in 1839. These four travelers found that the council fire brought from the Great Smokies in 1839 was still burning. They took coals from this fire. In a bucket lined with asbestos they brought these coals back to the Cherokees in the Great Smoky Mountains.

They would not trust this precious flame to burning coals alone. Instead, they fitted a case with tanks of bottled gas to guard and feed the flame which had traveled from North Carolina to Oklahoma and back again more than a century later. There is a spare tank of bottled gas kept always full and connected so that there is no danger of running out of fuel.

The keeping of the "eternal flame" is entrusted to one of the most honored men of the tribe. Arsene Thompson, his rugged face lined but smiling, is a preacher to the Cherokees and has at times been head of the tribal council. While he keeps alive the "eternal flame," he also keeps alive in the Cherokees that Christian love which has helped them to forgive the white man and call him friend.

And this is the inscription over the flame which the Cherokee Indians hope to keep burning forever:

This fire will burn forever as a symbol of "Friendship between the white man and the red man." It was kindled with a flame from a Cherokee Indian Council fire that has been burning in Oklahoma since 1839. The original fire was taken to Oklahoma when all but a remnant of the proud Cherokee nation was removed west over the infamous Trail of Tears. In May, 1951, four Cherokee tribal leaders from the Qualla Reservation retraced that trail of heartbreak taken by their ancestors and brought back five coals from the Oklahoma fire. One of these tribal leaders, Arsene Thompson, who plays Elias Boudinot in *Unto These Hills,* is the official caretaker of the flame. As a precaution against the flame dying, he keeps a companion fire burning at his home. Eternal Flame here at

Mountainside Theater was kindled from the century-old Oklahoma fire on June 23, 1951.

So the inscription ends. There is no word of blame for the white man who caused that flame to be carried to faraway Oklahoma on the Trail of Tears. As this fire burns, "symbol of friendship between the white man and the red man," we must feel humble before the Indian who has suffered and has forgiven.

The Girl with the Jack Knife

IF LITTLE AMANDA CROWE HAD TO CHOOSE BETWEEN A DOLL or a jack knife, she would have chosen the knife. Deciding between a knife and a fishpole would have been harder for this girl of the East Band of the Cherokee Indians. She would have taken them both.

Amanda remembers how she used to whittle on a chunk of buckeye or cherry wood as she followed the shady banks of the clear Oconaluftee River to her favorite fishing spots. Then into her pocket would go her knife and her half-whittled animal—a turtle, a wildcat, a deer, or a bear. She needed both her hands to angle for trout in the swift, clean water that flowed from the Great Smoky Mountains through Cherokee country in North Carolina.

Amanda Crowe began to whittle when she was five years old. To her, any piece of wood had inside it a hawk, a fox, a rabbit, or some other wild creature that needed only the little Indian girl and her busy jack knife to free it. Her mother saw her skill and let her spend much time whittling. Her uncle, Watty Chitolskey, was one of the best wood carvers of the East Band of the Cherokee tribe. He noticed little Amanda's skill with the knife. He saw her keen eye for the shapes and personalities of animals. So he showed her how to make lifelike figures from the woods that grew in Cherokee country at the edge of the beautiful mountains. Little Amanda was quick to learn. She used all the tricks her uncle taught her. She used them with her own imagination. The sheep or donkeys or owls that Amanda carved looked real, but they had something extra that was Amanda's own feeling about them.

Sometimes while Amanda was growing up, the teachers in the government school felt impatient with her. While she went through the six grades at Birdtown, the teachers had to remind her that it was pencils and books she must be learning to use—not always a jack knife. As soon as school was out for the day, she would be off with her fishpole over her shoulder and her jack knife busy in her hand.

When she went to junior and senior high school at Cherokee, the teachers had the same trouble. It was not that Amanda objected to books, but just that she liked carving and fishing better. Luckily there were teachers who understood. They felt there was an artist in the girl who liked to whittle. They thought the right training might make a really great artist grow from the Indian girl, just as Amanda herself could make lifelike animals grow from a chunk of pine or walnut.

One of Amanda's teachers was transferred to Chicago. She invited the girl to live with her and study art in the Chicago high school. Here Amanda showed such talent that she was given the chance to compete for a scholarship to study at the Chicago Art Institute. She won. After several years of studying there, she won a scholarship to study in another country and went to Mexico to learn about wood carving, sculpture, and other forms of art.

The little girl with the jack knife had grown into a true artist. She could take blocks of wood or stone and transform them into beautiful figures that people were glad to buy for decorations in lovely homes. The young Indian woman could have chosen to live almost anywhere and had a good position as a teacher of art. She could have set up her own studio, anywhere, and been paid well for her carving.

But Amanda Crowe remembered the many clear streams that poured down the sides of the Great Smoky Mountains and flowed through Cherokee country in North Carolina. She knew that many Indians who are well educated move off the reservations to use their skills. Amanda loved her Cherokee country, and she loved her Cherokee tribespeople. She remembered her friends of the Cherokee townships: Birdtown, Paint Town, Wolf Town, Soco, Yellow Hill, and Big Cove. She remembered how spring covered the Great Smokies with the pink, red, and white of laurel and rhododendron blossoms. She remembered that some Cherokee children had in them the same artistic ability that was in her own clever fingers. All they needed was someone to help them as Uncle Watty had helped her.

So, when the invitation came to return to Cherokee to teach wood carving, Amanda said "Yes." She was ready to go home and help her people. And everyone who knows her says she is the sort of teacher who can inspire anyone to create figures from chunks of buckeye, walnut, or wild cherry.

The Tears of the Yunwi Tsunsdi

A Legend of the Cherokee Indians

LONG AGO THE YUNWI TSUNSDI, OR "LITTLE PEOPLE," LIVED IN colonies in rocky caves in the Great Smoky Mountains that rise high in the land of the Cherokees. They were a happy and handsome elfin race, less than a foot and a half tall, with long hair that almost touched the ground. They were loved for their kind hearts and their habit of helping. There were many stories of their good deeds: lost children cared for and taken back to their homes, farmers waking in the morning to find their fields cleared while they slept, sick Cherokees cured of diseases that were beyond the art of the medicine men.

The Little People were seldom seen but sometimes heard. Faint and distant sounds of drums, dancing, and happy voices meant the Yunwi Tsunsdi were at play.

One day the Little People were enjoying themselves in a sunny clearing around a pool deep in the forests on the mountains. There was no human to disturb their play and make them fade into the shadows. There was no cloud to make them sad. Winter had gone and the beauty of spring was around them. The red buds of the maples were coming into leaf. The fragrance of trailing arbutus told where the pink, waxy blossoms were peeking through the dry oak leaves on the ground. The clean smell of warming earth brought songs to their lips, music to their dancing feet, and joy to their hearts.

Suddenly a strange messenger stood before them. To someone else he might have looked like one of the Little People, but to them he was quite different. It was plain that he had come from far away, from a land beyond the mountains and even beyond the seas.

At first the Yunwi Tsunsdi invited the stranger to share their happy play. Then they saw his face was darkened with sadness such as they had never seen. They tried to cheer him with their singing and their dancing. They tried to draw him into their gay circle about their elfin drums, but the sadness never flickered on the traveler's face.

One by one, the Little People stopped their play to stand silently before the stranger, awed that there could be such sorrow in a world of springtime beauty. They did not wish to share the gloom he felt, but they knew they must hear what he had come to tell them.

"I come from the Land of the Dawn. I have crossed a great ocean and a great land to come to you. I have news. You must hear because you have kind hearts and joy in helping."

The Little People stared at him, unwilling to hear but knowing that they must. "Tell us. We listen."

"In the faraway land from which I come, there lived a Man better than anyone who was ever born into this world. He was sent by the Great God Above. He loved all people: the sick, the poor, the weak, the sinful, as well as those who lived well. He loved the Great God Above so much that he was able to make people, just ordinary people, know God's goodness and greatness. People who talked with the Man were happier and kinder. The cowards became brave because of him. Cruel persons grew kind. The selfish thought of others instead of themselves. Wherever he went, the world was better."

"Then why are you so sad?" The Little People were ready to smile again. "It is good news that such a man has come into the world. Come rejoice with us. We will dance and sing more joyfully than ever because of this Man who makes people better."

But the messenger did not smile with them. The Little People saw that his face had lost none of its sadness. "Is there more?" they asked.

"There is more." The messenger was silent for a minute, his head bowed. Then he spoke in a voice so low that the Little People crowded one another to hear his words. "There were men in my land who were afraid of this good Man. They thought he was getting too strong because so many loved him. They feared their own power would grow smaller as his power grew bigger. He said he did not wish to be an earth king, but these men could not believe him. His heart was too kind and too pure for their dark hearts to understand."

"So what did they do?" The Little People were breathless for fear some evil had come to this Man who had the power to make people better. "What did they do to this good Man?"

"They sent soldiers to capture him," said the messenger. "The rulers could find no reason for punishing him, but, because they wanted to please the crowds, they sent him to a hill carrying a heavy wooden cross. They set the cross on the hilltop, and nailed him to it. He hung there on the cross till he died."

The kindly Yunwi Tsunsdi had grown to love the Man who was so good. The news that he had suffered was too much for them. All at once they began to weep tears of love for him. Because they were thinking of his cross, their tears were in the shape of the cross. Hundreds, even thousands, of tiny crosses fell from their eyes and were spread upon the ground about the deep pool in the mountain forest.

And to this day there is a place in the Great Smoky Mountains where the ground is covered with tiny stones in the shape of perfect crosses. These stones show no signs of cut or carving. They are as nature made them. Till some scientist gives a reason why the little stone crosses are in that spot and in no other, what better explanation do we have than the old Cherokee legend of the Little People of the mountains crying stone-cross tears because Christ had died on a cross?

Source: "The Fairy Crosses," in *Roaming the Mountains,* by John Parris (Asheville, N. C.: Citizen-Times, 1955).

The Possum's Tail

A Folk Tale of the Cherokee Indians

THIS IS WHAT THE OLD MEN TOLD ME WHEN I WAS A BOY.

In the old days the animals walked upright and talked like

men. They met about their council fires to pass laws, to plan festivals, or to settle quarrels. They met at their townhouse in a woodland clearing to feast or dance together.

Their herald was Tsistu the Rabbit, who was a big animal in those days. If there was to be a gathering, it was Rabbit who loped up hill and down to tell Awi the Deer, Yanu the Bear, Dayi the Beaver, and all of the other creatures of the forest when and where to meet. Though Rabbit was a tricky fellow, he was a good herald.

Once when Rabbit was shouting the call to a dance, he was not so cocky as usual. Till now he had swished his beautiful bushy tail jauntily as he ran through the woods. Today he had only a puff of white fur where his tail used to be. This was because he had been saucy to Yanu the Bear and then had not run fast enough to escape Bear's sharp claw.

"Come to the council and dance tonight at sunset," Rabbit called to Awahili the Eagle, perched high on a cliff.

"I will come." Eagle flapped wings and watched Rabbit back away to hide his stub of a tail. Rabbit was sure Eagle knew his story and was laughing at him.

He tried to face Awi and Deer, then Waya the Wolf, then Tsula the Fox, as he announced the evening gathering. But as Rabbit backed away from each, he heard snickers. Probably every animal in the Great Smoky Mountains knew that Bear had punished Rabbit by clawing off his beautiful tail.

No wonder Rabbit burned with jealousy when he found Sikwa Utsetsti the Possum combing the long, bushy tail of which he was tremendously proud. Rabbit's first thought was to punish Possum for his beautiful tail by passing him by. It would be more than bobtailed Rabbit could endure to see Possum at the dance parading his splendid tail. But Rabbit was too good a herald to skip any animal.

"Come to the council and dance tonight at sunset," he called to Possum.

Possum ran his comb through his tail again before answering, "May I have a special seat?"

"Why?" asked Rabbit.

"I want to sit where everyone can see this most beautiful tail in all the world." Because he was gazing at his own tail, Possum did not see the sly twinkle suddenly come to Rabbit's eyes.

"Of course you must have a special seat. I will arrange it myself." Rabbit's voice was sweet as honey.

"Thanks!" Possum curved his tail this way and that, looking at it so proudly that he missed the gleam in Rabbit's eye.

"Such a lovely tail needs the best care." Rabbit's voice oozed flattery. "Cricket is the cleverest hairdresser. I will send him to you so that your tail will be more beautiful than ever tonight."

Then off hurried Rabbit, so excited about his plan that he did not bother to back away from Dila the Skunk or Uksuhi the Blacksnake, as he called his message, "Come to the council and dance at sunset."

It was at the house of Talatu the Cricket that he stopped for a long whisper before he went chuckling through the woods inviting every bird, beast, snake, and insect to the gathering. Rabbit knew that Cricket, who was proud of being the best barber and hairdresser, would carry out his directions. Rabbit knew that Possum would come proudly to the council waving the bandaged tail about which Cricket would have ordered, "Keep this red ribbon binding your tail till you are at the council meeting. Then no burrs or snarls will spoil its beauty. Wait till you are seated on the special throne Rabbit is making for you. Then unbind the red ribbon and let your tail fluff out in all its gleaming beauty." And Rabbit knew that Possum would be so flattered by Cricket's attention that he would do exactly as he was told.

At sunset there was a great crackling of twigs and tramping of hoofs as the creatures bore down upon the clearing place where the council fire burned near the townhouse. Some of them wondered why there was a new throne of rocks built in the center.

Possum, however, did not wonder. He walked straight to it, holding high his tail with its binding of red ribbon.

The animals made short work of the the council meeting. Soon the drums were beating for the dance. "Who will be first?" Rabbit looked at Possum.

"I will." Possum stepped from his high seat and unloosed the red ribbon. Instead of looking at his tail, he watched the faces of the other animals, the better to enjoy their envy when they saw that his tail was more beautiful than ever.

"What do you think of my tail?" asked Possum in a loud voice as he began to dance. The animals shouted louder than he expected, but there was a strange sound to their shouting.

"Did you ever see longer, shinier fur?" asked conceited Possum, taking a turn around the circle. The animals shouted still louder. He had not expected such wild applause. He strutted more and more.

"Did you ever see a lovelier color?" Possum waved his tail and danced mincing steps. The shouting rose to a roar that sounded like laughter and jeers.

That was no way to admire a beautiful tail! Possum stared at them angrily. There was no doubt about it! They were laughing at him! Why?

Possum turned at last to look at his own tail. He expected to see a beautiful fluff of shining fur. Instead he saw a thin stringy tail as ropey as the tail of Rat or Lizard. He knew now that Cricket had clipped his hair as he bound on the red ribbon. And he could guess who had told Cricket to do it.

But knowing could not bring back his beautiful tail. Knowing could not bring back his old pride and vanity. There was nothing Possum could do but lie down on the ground with a shamed little grin on his face.

Never since then has Sikwa Utsetsti the Possum been conceited. He and all his grandchildren have worn bare tails and walked without pride. And ever since that day, Possum and all his grandchildren have curled on the ground with a silly grin on their faces when they think they are being watched.

The Race

A Folk Tale of the Cherokee Indians

THIS IS WHAT THE OLD MEN TOLD ME WHEN I WAS A BOY.

In the olden days the animals liked games, races, and all sorts of contests. Once they were arguing which could run faster, Awi the Deer or Tsistu the Rabbit. As you know, Rabbit then was big—not the little bunny we have nowadays. And in those days Deer's head was bare of antlers.

"Awi the Deer is the fastest runner in the forest," said some.

"Tsistu the Rabbit can hop as fast as Deer can run," said others.

"Let them race together," suggested Yanu the Bear. "Then we can know which goes faster."

"Let's have a prize—a pair of antlers," suggested Wahuhu the Screech Owl.

All the animals agreed, including Deer and Rabbit. Deer knew that no animal ever passed him when he was running in the forest. Rabbit knew that no animal could beat him in thinking up schemes for winning. So, both Deer and Rabbit dreamed of the antler-prize as they practiced running or hopping through the forest.

The course chosen for the race led through thick underbrush from one clearing to another. The antlers were set in the first clearing near the starting line. They were strong, many-pronged, and shining. Rabbit and Deer gazed at them hopefully.

"You will run through the thicket to the next clearing and back again," explained Bear. He had been appointed referee because the race was his idea. "Deer will start here. Rabbit will start there." Bear showed the spots, about ten feet apart, where the two would break into the vine-draped woodland.

The animals nodded. Deer and Rabbit nodded with them. Some animals were picturing how handsome Deer would be with the glistening branched antlers on his noble head. Others were thinking how silly Rabbit would seem with the antlers towering high between his long ears.

The time for the race drew nearer when Rabbit had a question: "May I run over the trail once before the race begins? I am not as familiar with this part of the mountains as Deer is."

The animals looked at Deer, questioning him.

"If you wish," he said pleasantly. Then Deer started nibbling tender leaves from a beech tree while he waited.

Rabbit hopped off into the vines and bushes that covered the forest ground. The animals watched the shaking of twigs and leaves till he was out of sight. Then all was still. The animals waited—and waited—and waited.

Some talked together. Squirrel began hunting for beechnuts to crack. Bear found some berries that tasted good. Skunk and Possum curled up in shady nooks and fell asleep. Robin carried a juicy worm, then another, and another to feed her hungry babies. Woodpecker went back to the holes he was tapping in the trunk of a maple tree.

"What has happened to Rabbit?" asked Bear with his mouth full of berries.

"It will be night before we begin our race." Deer looked at the sun sliding toward the skyline.

"Someone should follow Rabbit to see what has happened," suggested Wolf. "Perhaps he is in trouble. Or perhaps he is up to mischief."

"The one who follows should be able to slip up on him quietly," said Bear.

The animals chose Snake because he could slither under or over the vines and branches with never a sound. No sooner was he chosen than Snake uncoiled himself and slid silently into the thicket where Rabbit had disappeared. The animals stood at attention waiting for Snake to return.

They did not wait long. Just as noiselessly and just as swiftly as he had gone away, Snake glided back into the clearing.

"Where is Rabbit?" the animals asked in chorus.

"He's up to one of his tricks," Snake hissed. "With his sharp teeth he is cutting out the vines and the underbrush to make an easy trail for himself."

The animals looked at Deer to see him rage. But Deer's honest brown eyes were filled with surprise that any creature could be so deceitful. He was more sorry than angry.

The other animals stood like a circle of solemn judges, their eyes on the spot where Rabbit must appear.

Soon there was a waving in the vines and a crackling in the underbrush. Out bounded Rabbit, as perky as ever.

"Well, well, my good friends, it took longer than I expected." Rabbit talked fast, not noticing the stern faces. "What a course it is through that thick underbrush! You will find, my good friend Deer, that it is a harder race than you expected. Let's get started right away or we won't be through before night."

The animals stood, stern and silent. Rabbit looked from Bear to Owl to Possum to Wolf. One face was as solemn as another.

"What's the matter?" Rabbit tried to look innocent.

"Snake, you tell Rabbit what's the matter," said Bear.

And Snake told Rabbit. The more Rabbit tried to call it a lie, the more his judges looked coldly at him. There was not an animal in the forest who had not, at one time or another, been hurt by Rabbit's trickery.

Then all the animals looked at Bear, the referee. The race had been his idea. Let him say what should happen next.

"Rabbit!" Bear's voice was deep and growly. "Your trickery has lost you the chance to compete for the beautiful antlers.

By stooping to such cheating, you admitted that Deer could go faster than you."

Then Bear turned toward Deer and said, "Deer, you are swift as the rushing river or the lightning. You are honest as the sunlight. The prize is yours."

Then all the animals—except Rabbit—cheered as Deer bent his noble head and Bear fastened on it the prize of large and many-pronged antlers.

"Rabbit!" Bear had one more thing to say. "If you like to gnaw bushes so well, your prize is to earn your living gnawing bushes." And the animals cheered again.

Ever since that day, Tsistu the Rabbit has gnawed for his food. And ever since that day, Awi the Deer has bounded lightly through the forest wearing beautiful many-pronged antlers on his noble head.

The Ball Game

A Folk Tale of the Cherokee Indians

WHEN I WAS A BOY, THIS IS WHAT THE OLD MEN TOLD ME.

In the olden days the birds and the animals were great ball-players. Once the animals sent Tsistu the Rabbit with this message to the birds: "We challenge you to a great ball game —the birds against the animals."

"We accept your challenge. We will play against you," was the answer Rabbit carried from the birds to the animals.

A date and a place for the game was set. Both sides began to practice. Yanu the Bear was captain for the animals. Awahili the Eagle was captain for the birds.

When the time for the great ball game arrived, there was the usual ball dance to prepare for it. The animals danced on the clearing near the Oconaluftee River. The birds danced in the trees that lined its banks.

Looking down, the birds saw how the animals strutted and bragged. The animals were sure, so very sure, that the birds could not possibly win over them. They had Yanu the Bear, whose strength was known throughout the forest. They had Awi the Deer, whose slim legs could run faster than any creature in the world. They had Tuksi the Turtle, whose heavy shell protected him while it made a heavy weapon to batter the other team.

Listening, Eagle's team knew the animals might be right. The birds would fight their hardest, but none of them felt like strutting or bragging. They saw little hope of winning the victory.

The birds were perched in the treetops, fluffing their feathers, waiting for the referee's call to begin the game. Suddenly they realized they were not alone. Two furry little creatures were pattering modestly along the branch toward them. They stopped in front of Eagle.

"Please," squeaked their little voices in unison, "may we play in the ball game? May we play on your side?"

"You?" exclaimed Eagle. "You are not birds. Each of you has four feet. You have fur instead of feathers. You belong with the animals."

"We tried to play on their side," squeaked the little thing with black fur, "but they laughed at us. They said we were too small to play with great animals like Deer, Bear, and Turtle. Their laughter was cruel."

The little creatures were so humble but so eager that the birds took pity on them.

"If you had wings, you could play on our side," said Eagle. The other birds nodded kindly.

"Perhaps we could make wings," squeaked the creature with gray fur.

"There's not much time!" Then Eagle called to his team, "Have we any way to make wings for these two little things?"

The birds fluttered about till one of them had an idea.

"The drums," exclaimed Sasa the Goose. "The dance is over. We can tear pieces of leather from the drums."

So for the little black creature they made wings of the groundhog skin that covered the drum. They fastened them to his front legs.

"We will call you Tlameha the Bat," announced Awahili the Eagle. "Now let's see what you can do with a ball."

Eagle tossed the ball. Little Bat dodged and circled, catching it and throwing it. Not once did he let it fall to the ground. His quick darts made the birds cheer and flutter their praise.

"Good!" said Eagle. "You may play on our team."

While Bat was practicing with the ball, the birds were making wings for the little gray creature. There was no groundhog skin left on the drum, so they had to think of another way. With their beaks the birds took hold of its fur on each side and pulled. They strained and they tugged till they had stretched the skin between its front and hind legs.

"Not really wings," admitted Eagle, inspecting the stretched skin, "but perhaps you can soar with them. Let's see if you can catch and carry the ball."

Eagle tossed. The little gray creature bared its sharp teeth and sprang at the ball. Catching it, he soared through the air carrying it to a distant tree.

"Splendid!" praised Eagle. "We will call you Tewa the Flying Squirrel. You may play on our team."

Just then the referee called for the game to begin. Eagle explained the rules quickly to his new players, pointing out the goal posts, a pair at either end of the playing field. "We try to carry the ball between the goal posts near the river. The animals try to carry it through the other pair. Get the ball whenever you can. Keep it away from the animals. Carry it toward our goal posts."

"We'll do our best," squeaked Bat and Flying Squirrel as the game began.

The ball had scarcely gone into play when Flying Squirrel caught it and went soaring from treetop to treetop. He tossed it to Hawk. It went from bird to bird. Whenever one of the birds missed, Bat, darting and circling near the ground, caught it before any animal could get claws on it.

Bat seemed to be everywhere. The animals running madly back and forth looked up at the strange little creature and wondered if he could be the one who had made them laugh. Perhaps they were too sure of their own strength when they laughed at his weakness.

Flying Squirrel, too, was in the thick of the game. He carried the ball in long swoops ever closer to the goal. The animals tried in vain to get their paws on the ball. They stared angrily at him. They recognized he was the second little creature who had begged to play on their side. They wished they had not been so proud of themselves and so scornful of him.

Their panting and their writhing did the animals no good. For all their strutting and boasting before the game, the strong arms of Bear were of no more use than the tough shell of Turtle or the fleet legs of Deer. The two little creatures they had scorned kept the ball away from them till it was finally carried through the goal posts for the birds' victory.

And ever since that day, both birds and animals have had great respect for the wings of Tlameha the Bat and Tewa the Flying Squirrel.

The Kingfisher's Wish

A Folk Tale of the Cherokee Indians

THIS IS WHAT THE OLD MEN TOLD ME WHEN I WAS A BOY.

In the olden days, Tsulu the Kingfisher was the unhappiest of birds. He had no way of supplying himself with his favorite food, fresh fish from the flowing streams of the Great Smokies. Sasa the Goose and Kawana the Duck had strong webbed feet. They could swim on ponds and streams, diving down to grab anything that pleased their appetites. Tskwayi the Heron had a long, sharp bill. He could stand long-legged in shallow water, darting suddenly to catch fish that swam too close.

But poor Kingfisher had neither webbed feet nor long, sharp bill. He used to sit on a branch overhanging the Oconaluftee River and watch the fish swimming in the clear water. His stubby little beak would hang open in hunger for the sweet-tasting morsels swimming in the rushing stream, but never a chance did he have to catch them.

One day while Tsulu the Kingfisher was perched on his favorite maple branch, he heard a great fluttering and bird-scolding a few trees away. He was too sorry for himself to pay any attention.

An hour or so later he was still on the same branch gazing longingly down into the clear water when the Flicker joined him. Her wings drooped sadly. Two sorrier birds could not be found in all the Great Smoky Mountains.

"What's the matter with you?" Kingfisher forgot to pity himself for a minute.

"A terrible thing has happened." Flicker's voice was woeful.

"Tell me!" Kingfisher snapped out of his own dumps when he saw another bird in trouble deeper than his own. "Perhaps I can help."

"The Little People said you would help," said Flicker. "They sent me to you."

Kingfisher hopped along the branch closer to the sad Flicker. "Tell me all about it."

"I left my four beautiful baby birds in their nest while I flew away to find food for them." Flicker wiped her eye with one big wing. "When I came back, I found Blacksnake coiled in the nest. He had eaten two of my beautiful babies—feathers, claws, beaks, and all. He was waiting till he had room in his stomach to eat the other two. I flew at him. I screamed at him and pecked at him. He only hissed his scorn of me."

"So that was the noise I heard in yonder tree." Kingfisher's voice was sympathetic. "I'd like to help, but how can I? I'm no bigger than you. My rattle-song is no louder than your hammer-song. And as to beaks, yours is twice as strong and sharp as my poor bill. If Blacksnake hissed his scorn of you, he would hiss louder and more scornfully at me. Get Crane or Heron to help you with their fine, strong bills."

"But the Little People sent me to you!" Flicker insisted.

"Let me go and ask why." Kingfisher flew off toward the caves where the Little People lived. He knew there was no time to waste. Someone must drive Blacksnake from the nest before he devoured the last of the baby birds.

Kingfisher knew the rocky cave near a pond where lived the kindhearted Yuñwi Tsundsi, the Little People. He flew toward them softly, careful not to frighten them. They were watching for him. They were handsome little elves with long hair that tickled their heels when they walked.

"Why did you tell Flicker I would save his babies?" Kingfisher didn't waste time on polite greetings.

"Are you brave enough to fight Blacksnake?" asked one who seemed to be leader of the Little People.

"I am not afraid," answered Kingfisher, "but how can I fight him? Look at my poor blunt bill! It is the most useless bill a bird ever owned."

"We will give you a spear to hold in your bill," said the spokesman for the Little People. While he was saying that, one of the others waded into the water, looking down till he saw what he was seeking. Then he stooped and came up with a tugaluna fish in his hand. It was a small spotted fish with a long mouth as sharp as a spear.

Right away Kingfisher knew what to do. With a triumphant rattle he grabbed the fish in his blunt bill, holding it so that the spear-sharp mouth pointed forward. As he flew away, he heard the tuneful cheers of the Little People. He heard their drums beating and their tiny feet dancing in triumph over his own quick understanding and daring. He could hear the drums, the singing, and the dancing feet following under him as the Little People marched to watch his fight with Blacksnake.

Kingfisher did not wait for them. He flew toward Flicker's nest as fast as strong wings would carry him. He must help his friend. He felt strong for the fight because the Little People trusted him and had given him a weapon.

There was Blacksnake filling the nest so full that the two baby birds were in danger of being crushed before they were eaten. Blacksnake was uncoiling himself and snapping his jaws. He seemed about ready for another feathered tidbit.

But his mouth never touched the baby birds. There was a flapping of strong wings over the nest. Kingfisher swooped on Blacksnake so violently that the fish-spear held in the bird's stubby beak pierced a hole clear through the snake's head. Then Flicker joined Kingfisher in rolling the dead snake from the nest.

On the ground below the tree, there was the triumphant beating of tiny drums and the proud singing of tiny voices.

"You are a brave bird, and kindhearted," called the Little People. "You forgot your own troubles when you found someone needing your help. What can we do to reward you? Have you some wish?"

"Only one wish in all the world." As Kingfisher spoke, the tugaluna fish fell down into the stream. "I wish for a bill as long and as sharp as the tugaluna fish."

"You have earned your wish," said the Little People.

Then as they drummed and danced and sang below him, Kingfisher felt his stubby beak grow as long and as sharp as the tugaluna fish. And ever since that day Tsulu the Kingfisher has been the happiest of birds. Now when he sits on his favorite branch overhanging his favorite pond or stream, he can peer into the clear water and then, rattling in his throat, he can swoop down and catch a tasty fish in his long, sharp beak.

STORIES OF THE PHILIPPINES

Because this book is being prepared in the Philippines, it is natural to give these beautiful islands a section of their own. Most of these stories are based on true-life incidents of today reported by workers in the church. There is also a story in the manner of folklore and another which tells of a hero in the early days of Protestantism.

The Oil or the Book

ZAIDAN, A GIRL OF THE BAGOBO TRIBE, STEPPED DOWN THE LADDER from her bark house in the hills near Davao in Mindanao of the Philippines. Her light brown skin was clean from a bath in the cold stream that flowed from her hills to the plains where the lowlanders lived.

Down the ladder after Zaidan came her mother and her little brother. They, too, were fresh from a bath in the stream and wore clean clothes of coarsely woven striped cotton.

With sure, free strides the three walked the rough mountain trail that led past all the bark huts of their Bagobo barrio in the hills. They did not notice the beautiful view from the clearings. They lived every day with beauty of tropical vines, trees, flowers, and birds.

"Mother," Zaidan began the question that was bothering her. "Where is Father? Will he come to church with us?"

"We cannot wait for him." Zaidan's mother did not seem

ready to answer her daughter's question. She added something that seemed to give her a little comfort. "Anyway, he has been baptized."

"He was baptized," agreed Zaidan, "but after a few times he did not go to church any more. Where does he go now? He is away from home for many hours. Where does he go?"

Zaidan's mother did not answer. It was her father that answered. After a few more steps along the trail they saw him. He was in the clearing in front of one of the high bark houses, squatting on the ground in a circle of other men from the Bagobo tribe. In front of them was a flicker of lighted wick burning in coconut oil. The men were droning a pagan chant in worship of the oil.

"Aren't you coming to church with us, Father?" Zaidan asked, even though she knew the answer. He looked up at his daughter, but did not miss a beat of the chant. He did not reply. Instead he looked back at the flame of the sacred oil.

The little brother ran to his father and squatted on the ground beside him. He stared at the flame as he saw the men doing. With a little cry of horror his mother picked up her child and swung him to her shoulder. Then she grasped Zaidan by the hand. Together they hurried along the trail toward the church which stood in the next barrio.

Zaidan was ready to cry. She had been so happy when her father had been baptized into their church. For weeks he had been kinder and happier than she had ever seen him. He took better care of his family. But lately things had changed again. He had been away from home more, and when he was at home, he was no longer kind and pleasant. Now Zaidan knew why he was different. He had gone back to the pagan worship.

"Why?" was all Zaidan could say as she ran to keep up with her mother's long steps. "Why?"

Her mother understood what she wanted to ask. "I think it is because we cannot read. He has been ashamed that he does not know enough to hold the hymnbook right side up. He is ashamed that he cannot answer questions in the class of new members. When the pastor tells us what to study in the Bible, we cannot. It is impossible to remember everything we hear. We should read it again in order to learn. But we cannot read. To worship the oil your father does not need to learn anything. He does not even need to think. He feels that he must worship something, so he takes the easy way."

Zaidan understood. She knew how it felt to be behind her class in the public school because she missed so many days.

"I'll try harder to learn at school," she promised. "I'll go every day and study hard. Then I can teach you and Father how to read."

"That will be good." Her mother almost smiled again. "Let's hope you can teach us before it is too late."

They were in sight of their church now, built on its posts high above the ground that was wet so much of the time. Its roof was of dried cogon grass, its walls and floors of bamboo. They saw a young man, a stranger, going in the door with the pastor. He was a lowlander, not one of the Bagobo tribe. They could tell by the way he dressed.

Zaidan, her mother, and her little brother sat on one of the wooden benches near the back of the church. The service began as usual. Soon the pastor introduced the visitor, a student from Silliman University who was going to spend his vacation in their hills. And when Zaidan heard what he was going to do for them, she could hardly hold herself from jumping on her bench and clapping her hands and shouting for joy.

"Anybody who wants to learn to read can come to the church every day. There will be classes every morning and every evening," the new young man was explaining. "Do not think it will be too hard for you. Do not think you are too old, or too tired. We have an easy way to learn—just a few words at a time from big charts with pictures. Soon you will be able to read from primers, then from storybooks written especially for you, then from your hymnbooks and Bibles."

On the way home from church Zaidan ran ahead of her mother. She wanted to be the first to tell her father that he could learn to read.

There is not time to tell everything that happened in that little Bagobo barrio in the hills that summer. We must skip to the end of the story which you have probably guessed already.

It is a Sunday morning a few months later. Zaidan, Sunday-clean, again comes down the ladder from her bark house. This time she is followed by her mother and her little brother *and her father,* all just as Sunday-clean as Zaidan from their baths in the cold mountain stream.

Together they walk past the bark huts of their barrio in the hills. They walk down the trail to the place where the men are squatting on the ground sounding their chants in worship of the oil that burns in front of them. Zaidan's father greets his neighbors politely. He tells them proudly where he is going. But he does not so much as glance at the flame. With steady stride he leads his family along the trail to the little church of bamboo and cogon.

Proudly they follow him down the aisle to one of the front benches. Sitting between their parents, Zaidan and her little brother watch them pick up their hymnbooks and Bibles—the books they have learned to read.

To Market

NENET AND MANUEL HAD BEEN TO MARKET MANY TIMES WITH Mother. When she needed only one or two things, they went alone to the little grocery store at the corner of their block in the wide and beautiful city of Manila in the Philippines. But they had never gone alone to the big covered market where people came every day to spread their wares on tables, or in booths, or on the ground.

"I am very busy today," Mother said. "I have not time to go to market."

"Manuel and I can go to Pedring's store for you," offered Nenet.

"But I have a long list to buy," said Mother. "Pedring's prices are higher than prices in the Quiapo market."

"We can go to Quiapo for you." Manuel stood tall to show that he was really big enough to go alone with Nenet.

Mother looked at her children steadily. She thought of the ride by bus or jeepney, of the many winding streets that looked alike, of the crowds in the big covered market place. Then she saw how tall they both stood, waiting for her answer.

"I'm sure you can go alone," she said.

The she handed each of them a big marketing bag woven of buri palm. To Manuel she gave six pesos to carry in his safest pocket. To Nenet she gave the list of groceries.

"If you shop carefully, there will be some money left," she said. "You have not had a treat for a long time. Save twenty centavos for your jeepney fare home. Then you may spend what is left for sweets, or toys, or whatever you wish."

Manuel and Nenet were discussing how they would spend the extra money while they stood at the corner by Pedring's store waiting for a bus marked "Quiapo." They stopped long enough in their talk of candy, Yo-yos, balls, and dolls to wave their hands at a thin little girl who was looking out the upstairs window over the grocery store.

"Poor Angie," said Nenet to Manuel. "She has been sick for weeks. She never gets outdoors to play. She hasn't anyone to play with her."

"She never has fun like we do," agreed Manuel, "going to market and everything."

Just then they saw the jeepney labeled "Quiapo." They were glad it was one of the new ones painted blue with designs of yellow, not one of the old ones that looked like a worn-out army jeep. The driver stopped with a jerk, waiting just long enough for them to climb in, and was off with another jerk.

"Quiapo market," they told him as they reached over his shoulder to pay their fare. But they watched landmarks, too. Between dodging other jeepneys and winding his way among buses and trucks, and stopping while passengers got off and on, he might forget where two children wanted to go.

"Psst!" whistled Manuel. The jeepney jerked to a stop only a few steps from the entrance to the big covered market. They passed the shops that lined the sidewalk, and went into the big dim building where food was for sale on every side. What fun it was to walk up and down the aisles between tables and booths. Everything smelled so good. It looked so good. If the children had not had Mother's list to follow, they would have bought all sorts of interesting things. But they must buy the fish, rice, soap, matches, garlic, bananas, and other everyday things that Mother needed. The children went from booth to booth to find where they could get the most for their money. They remembered that the size of their treat depended on how well they shopped and bargained.

At last the buri bags were full and Manuel's six pesos had been changed into a pile of small red, green, and brown pieces of paper money. Back in Manuel's pocket went a twenty-centavo piece to pay for the jeepney fare home. Then the children bent their heads over the remaining paper money as they counted.

"A peso and sixty centavos!" The children walked from the food market onto the bright sidewalk. "We can get a wonderful treat for that. We won't have to choose between toys and sweets. We can buy both."

Then Nenet stopped smiling for just a minute. "When we are having such good luck, I feel more sorry than ever for poor Angie, alone in her house with no fun and no playmates."

Manuel could not think of anything to say.

Up and down the busy sidewalk of Quiapo walked Nenet and Manuel—slowly in front of shops that sold toys or sweets—quickly in front of stores that sold cloth or tools. They turned down side streets, being careful not to lose their way.

"Tuloy kayo!" they heard a harsh voice inviting someone to come in. "Tuloy kayo!"

Not having any special place to go, they walked toward the strange voice. They wanted to see who was so eager to have them, or somebody else, come in. They forgot to linger by the woman who sold sugared pili nuts, or the man who sold ice cream cones, or the shop that sold harmonicas and balloons.

"Tuloy kayo!" The voice was inviting them into a store that was all a-twitter with a medley of smaller voices. As the children drew nearer, the chirps and chatters were louder.

"A pet shop!" Nenet and Manuel entered, then walked between rows of cages. In the low cages, monkeys were scratching, chewing, and chattering. In the middle cages, birds were twittering—little red finches and bigger gray and white lovebirds. In the highest cages, yellow canaries trilled sweet tunes. On the other side of the store were big glass tubs where colored fish swam. And in the center of the shop, with their legs tied to a post, were huge blue and green parrots croaking "Tuloy kayo" in their harsh voices.

Nenet and Manuel laughed to find who called them into the pet shop. But they did not laugh long. They began reading the price tags.

"Only a peso and twenty centavos for a pair of finches!" said Nenet. The other birds cost more. Manuel fingered the paper money in his pocket. He knew it was more than enough.

"There would need to be a cage," Nenet remembered.

The petshop keeper noticed them. "There are some cheap cages made of bamboo strips. They cost only a few centavos."

Nenet and Manuel did not ask each other if the birds were what they wanted to buy as their treat. They knew. It took only a few minutes of bargaining to persuade the petshop owner to let them have two finches and a cage for the money they could spend.

"Salamat," the parrot was thanking them while Manuel counted out the paper money. Nenet chose the two small finches that seemed the prettiest and the most friendly.

The two children could scarcely believe their good luck as they walked from the shop with their new pets. They hurried back to the main sidewalk and stopped a jeepney headed for their home.

They hoped the driver would be more careful than usual. Their birds must not be bounced too much. Stepping from the jeepney they waved gaily at Angie's pale face. She was still peering out her window over Pedring's store. Angie smiled at the birds—a slow, sad smile.

"After we've taken the groceries home," suggested Manuel, "we can go back and show the birds to Angie."

"Yes," agreed Nenet. "She'll love looking at them. She never has any fun."

"It must be lonesome staying in the house all the time with no playmates," said Manuel.

The children did not speak again till they reached home. They were thinking about the same thing. Each was sure what the other was thinking. They knew what to say when their mother came to the top of the stairs to greet them.

"Beautiful!" Mother sounded happy at their choice. "Pet birds are better than toys or sweets! They will look lovely singing in the front window."

"Not in *our* front window!" Manuel looked at Nenet.

She nodded at her brother. Then she said, "They will look lovely in Angie's front window over Pedring's store!"

Then Mother looked even happier than before.

Lito Finds His Talent

LITO LEANED ON THE BAMBOO FENCE THAT MARKED THE YARD around the small wooden church with its roof of dried palm leaves. It rested his arms to lean on the fence instead of his crutches for a few minutes.

He was glad he had dared come as far as the church fence today. Yesterday he had stood across the rutted road to watch the boys and girls under the big mango tree in the church yard. People, cars, and carabao on the road kept shutting off his view of what was going on.

Now he was so near the Bible class that he could see the big colored pictures the teacher was showing. The children called her Miss Naomi. She did not belong to their village but came in the big red bus every morning to teach vacation church school. Lito, even from across the road, liked her soft voice and her friendly smile. Now, leaning on the fence, he could hear the stories she was telling about the pictures.

Lito hoped nobody would notice him and start teasing him about his ragged clothes, or his twisted and useless leg, or his skinny dog, or his father who wasted time and pesos on cock-fights. They might tease him because he had never been to school and could not read or write, even though he was old enough to be in fourth or fifth grade. The barrio children seemed to delight in finding new and cruel ways to show he was not good enough to play with them.

Lito shifted his weight and leaned more heavily on the fence of bamboo poles. It creaked. The teacher and children turned to see what made the noise. Lito picked up his crutches and hobbled away.

"Come back!" called Miss Naomi. "Come into the church-yard with us! Do not run away!"

But Lito's crutches kept tapping on the road that was hard in the brief dry season that comes to the Philippines in March, April, and May. His crutches tapped and tapped till he reached his own nipa hut, the smallest and dirtiest and shakiest in the barrio. Some said there was no poorer hut in the whole province, and perhaps they spoke the truth.

It was the next day before Lito limped quietly toward the church again. He waited till the boys and girls were all there, so there would be nobody in the houses or on the road to make fun of him. This time he did not lean on the fence even to rest his arms that were tired by his crutches. He stood close to the fence, leaning on his crutches.

He could see the picture Miss Naomi was holding in front of the children, who sat in a circle under the mango tree. He could hear her story. It was about a very kind and good man named Jesus, who loved children, animals, poor people, sick people—everybody.

"See the lame boy in the picture!" Miss Naomi was holding up a bright colored picture showing a boy with crutches. "That little lame boy knew that Jesus loved him. He knew . . ."

But Lito missed the next words because of the noise of his own crutches and good foot as he hobbled nearer to the gate of the churchyard. He stood by the bamboo gate listening to the song the boys and girls were singing:

Long ago the little children
  Gathered close at Jesus' knee,
For his kindly smile said gently,
  "I love them and they love me."

Come and listen to the story,
  Friend of children still is He,
Listen then and whisper softly,
  "I love Him and He loves me."

Lito never knew how it happened. He did not plan to walk through that church gate. But there he was in his rags, leaning against the very mango tree under which the children were sitting in their clean Bible-school clothes. And, most surprising of all, he was singing with the children as they sang their song a second time: "I love them and they love me."

He saw Miss Naomi look at him and whisper to the girl who sat next to him. But to Lito's great surprise, he was not afraid. He sang through the second verse with the children: "I love Him and He loves me."

"Oh, Lito!" said Miss Naomi, who had asked his name from the girl next to her. "You have a lovely voice."

"You sing better than any of us, Lito!" said one of the boys. "I wish you'd come to Bible school every day and help us sing."

"Yes, Lito," said the children. "We want you!"

Lito looked at the boys who used to tease him. He looked at the girls who used to giggle at his tattered clothes and mended crutches. They were smiling at him. "We want you, Lito." He wondered if it was church or Miss Naomi's stories about Jesus that made the difference.

"Let's sing some more—with Lito to help us," said Miss Naomi.

Then Lito forgot that he had never been to school because of his crutches, and shabby clothes, and the cost of schoolbooks. He forgot that this was the first time he had ever dared hobble inside the bamboo fence of the churchyard. He forgot that he was the boy nobody liked and everybody teased. Now Lito was the boy that everybody wanted. He was the boy with the lovely voice that could help the others with their singing. He hobbled near Miss Naomi and sat down in the circle with the other boys and girls.

After class Lito went home singing in time to the tapping of his crutches: "Come and listen to the story . . ."

He told his tired mother, his thin brothers and sisters, and his lazy father all that he had heard at Bible school. He was happy that they let him go back to the church the next day and the day after and on and on as long as vacation school lasted. He was still happier when they came to the program on the last day of the school to hear him sing a song all by himself.

But he was happiest of all when they decided to go to church with him one Sunday—and kept on going Sunday after Sunday.

The Other Half of the House

THE FOUR MANSUETO CHILDREN SAT ON THE LADDER-LIKE STEPS OF their side of the two-family house to watch the new neighbors moving into the other half of the house. Pedro, the two-year-old, sat on the top step where he could dodge quickly through the door to Mother and safety. Six-year-old Alicia's black curly head was just below his small bare feet. Pepita, who was eight, was brave enough to sit halfway down on step number six. Carlos, the big brother, sat only three steps from the ground, where he could protect the younger children and see the most. He had a good view, not only of the new neighbors' steps and yard and door, but also of the busy under-the-house space which is so useful in the rain-rich Philippines.

The new neighbors smiled at the four Mansuetos and tried to start a conversation while carrying mats, chairs, tables, kettles, dishes, and chests up their steps so close to the watching children. But Carlos, Pepita, Alicia, and Pedro were too shy to answer—too shy even to smile. They just sat in a solemn row and stared with dark, wondering eyes.

The next day and the next the children watched. Sometimes they watched from their steps, sometimes from the shade of the breadfruit tree in their half of the yard, and sometimes through the peekholes in the wall of woven palm fibers that separated their rooms from the rooms of their new neighbors. The children knew everything that happened in the other half of the house. They knew when the boy and girl went to school, when the mother went to market, and when the father went off to talk with people.

Once or twice Carlos and Pepita followed the father and found that he talked with people on the street, or in the market place, or in homes. They heard him inviting people to come to his house the next Sunday morning. They thought he asked them to come to church in his house but they knew they must have misunderstood. They knew that a church was a big building with a sad-faced statue in its yard and many images and candles in a big dim room. The other half of the house was just like theirs—not a bit like a church.

The neighbors invited the Mansuetos for Sunday morning also. Father and Mother Mansueto shook their heads while Pedro hid behind his mother, the little girls stared, and Carlos whispered a polite "No, thank you, sir."

On the fourth day, Sunday, a strange thing happened in the half-house of the new neighbors. Just before nine o'clock in the morning, people began climbing up their steps. First came the owners of the variety store at the corner. Then came the schoolteacher and his family. Then came the grandmother of their friend Rosa, a man who drove a brown jeepney, the lady dentist with her three little girls, the man that worked in the drugstore, the potter who made clay pots and bowls, the cleaning woman from the big house with the star-apple tree, a farmer who tied his carabao under the house, the boy who sold them little hard rolls for breakfast every morning, a policeman in a clean gray uniform. The children began to wonder if the split-bamboo floor could hold so many people. Instead of worrying, however, they enjoyed the gay and friendly talk coming from the open door and wide windows.

Suddenly the talking stopped. It was very still. Then the children heard one voice speaking slowly.

The little Mansuetos scrambled up their steps to join their parents, whose ears were close to the woven walls. They could hear every word in the other half of the house.

The voice stopped speaking. Someone hummed a tune.

Then there was singing. At first it was hard to understand the words. Soon their ears grew used to the sounds. The Mansuetos heard the people singing about someone named Jesus. The words "We would see Jesus" came often. It was a good song. The little Mansuetos could hum it on their side of the thin wall while their mother kept time with her head and their father tapped his foot. There were other songs. Then they heard the voice again, the voice of the father of the new neighbors' family.

"We hope to have a church building of our own some day," he said. "Till then our church can meet here in our house."

In the weeks that followed, the peekholes in the woven walls grew larger from much use. There was one just the right height for Carlos, lower peekholes for each of his sisters, a very low one for little Pedro, and two high ones for their father and mother. The songs sung loudly on the other side of the wall were sung softly on the Mansuetos' side: "We Would See Jesus," "For the Beauty of the Earth," "Praise God, from Whom All Blessings Flow." The sermons, prayers, and Bible readings came clearly through the thin wall. So did the stories told especially for children who came early for their own Sunday school.

Finally, one Sunday morning, Mother Mansueto dressed Alicia and Pepita in their newest and starchiest dresses. She told Carlos to scrub very clean at the cold faucet in the sink, and to put on his best shirt and shorts. The children could guess what was coming before she said, "You may go to the other side of the house this morning."

"You and Father will come with us? No?" asked Carlos.

"No. He will go to watch the cockfights soon, and I must stay here to take care of Pedro," she said.

Carlos reminded her, "Some children as small as Pedro will be there." He knew she was making excuses because she was afraid to go to a Protestant church, even to one that met in a half-house.

Three shy, clean children walked down the Mansueto steps

and up their neighbors' steps that morning. They found the welcome and the happiness that a church always has for visitors or newcomers. The children had much to tell when they went back to their own half of the house.

They did not finish telling it that day. For five more days they were humming the songs, repeating the stories, and talking about next Sunday. Sometimes they heard their parents whispering together, very seriously.

"What would the priest say?" the father would ask.

"He will never miss us," the mother would answer. "You know we never go to his church except on fiesta days when everybody goes."

"Let the children go a while longer," the parents would agree, "and see what happens."

So, Sunday after Sunday the children went to church in the other side of the house. They went during the week, too, for play and for classes. And all the time their parents saw them grow happier, kinder, more quick to obey.

Finally came the Sunday when Carlos, Alicia, and Pepita were not alone climbing down their steps and up their neighbors' steps. Mother Mansueto led Pedro with her. Father Mansueto grumbled a little about wasting time but he went up the neighbors' steps too.

They must have liked what they found, because the whole family has been going to church ever since.

This true story happened on the Philippine island of Leyte almost twenty years ago. (The only part that is not true is the name of the family.) All but one of the Mansuetos sit in church pews every Sunday to hear the minister preach. But one of them, Carlos, is in the pulpit of a church near Manila every Sunday. He is studying to become a minister. He has a church of his own while he is studying.

The church where Carlos Mansueto preaches has a lovely building among the palms, a musical bell, a good organ and choir, pews with plenty of red-covered hymnbooks, a pleasant room for Sunday school classes. Carlos is glad about all this, but he knows that it is not the building that makes a church. He will never forget how he peeked and listened through a thin woven wall into a room where a church with no building of its own was worshiping God.

The Hidden Treasure

LIFE IN THE HOME OF THE BOY NICHOLAS ZAMORA WAS ALWAYS A thing of danger and adventure. In those days when the Philippine Islands were ruled by Spain, there was one sure way to get into trouble—to say or do something the powerful Spanish friars did not like. Because the Zamora family dared think for themselves, they were always in danger of displeasing the friars.

Nicholas' uncle, Jacinto Zamora, was one of three brave Filipino priests who had been cruelly killed on order of the Spanish friars in 1872 for daring to say what they thought and to do what they believed. But even that did not frighten the Zamoras.

Every evening as soon as it was dark, they did something that was forbidden. Nicholas' father, Paulino Zamora, was careful to see that they were not caught doing it. In fact, he moved his family from the big city of Manila to a safer town in the provinces where he would have a better chance to keep his secret. It was not that Paulino was a coward. It was just that he could do more for his fellow Filipinos alive than clubbed to death for disagreeing with the ruling friars.

Every evening after the supper of fish and rice and vegetables, the Zamoras pulled down the shutters that covered their won-dows and closed the doors through which someone might look in from the darkness. Then, by the light of their torch, Paulino Zamora took the family's greatest treasure from the place where it was securely hidden.

Nicholas knew the story of the smuggling of that treasure

secretly into the Philippine Islands from Spain. Paulino Zamora had told a sea captain, "I will give you a hundred pesos if you will buy a Bible in Spain and bring it to me." One hundred pesos was a great deal of money, but Paulino's wish for a Bible was great.

Months later the sea captain had come secretly to Paulino. He was careful that nobody should know that he was carrying the forbidden book to the Zamora home. The Spanish friars did not want the Filipinos to read the Bible, because it made men think. If they read the Bible, they would learn that men were free and that men could talk directly to God without paying the Spanish friars to pray for them. Imprisonment or death waited for anyone found owning a Bible.

That was why the Zamoras moved from the city. That was why the shutters and doors were closed every evening before the Zamora family took their hundred-peso Bible from its hiding place to read its words that were so new and thrilling.

The boy Nicholas and his brothers listened as carefully as their parents. Nicholas had a quick mind for memorizing. In the daytime he could remember what his father had read the night before. Listening at night and remembering by day, Nicholas filled his mind with stories and teachings of the Bible. He was not satisfied with a few memory verses. He had memory chapters, even memory books.

So Nicholas grew up with the Bible in his mind and in his heart. Troubles came to his family, but always the Bible was kept hidden. Paulino Zamora was arrested because he displeased the Spanish friars, but the friars did not find the Bible.

When Nicholas was a young man, the revolution came. The people of the Philippine Islands fought for their freedom from Spain. Nicholas, who loved freedom, fought with them. As he went off to join the men fighting for liberty, he carried with him a treasure carefully wrapped so that nobody could guess it was his Spanish Bible.

Nicholas did not need to hide this Bible from his fellow fighters. They loved freedom also. They were glad to hear him read from the book that the Spanish friars had forbidden to them. The soldiers would gather around Nicholas and his book when they were resting from battle. Many of them did not know Spanish. He had to translate from Spanish into their dialect as he read to them. Because he knew so much of the Bible by heart, he could recite chapters of it when he could not have the Bible with him.

Finally peace came to the Philippines. Also there came new rulers, the Americans, who said that every man had the right to worship as he wished. The American soldiers had their chaplains and Protestant services. Nicholas worshiped with them. He asked the chaplain to hold services for Filipinos in the language they could understand.

At that first Protestant service, Nicholas stood up and told what the Bible had meant to him as he was growing up in a home where the forbidden book was the greatest treasure. When he finished talking about the Bible, he prayed, "Blessed God, we thank thee that the Book is open to us. Praise God, it is no longer a crime to read the Bible." The listening people were so impressed by what he said that they did a strange thing. Instead of saying "Amen," they clapped their hands.

The name of Nicholas Zamora is a great name in the history of the Protestant church in the Philippines. When the first Protestant missionaries arrived, soon after the islands became American territory in 1898, they found a few Filipino Protestants waiting to welcome them. The first Filipinos to become members of the Protestant church were Paulino Zamora and his three sons.

It was Nicholas who became the first Filipino preacher and one of the greatest. It is no wonder that he had messages to share. His mind and his heart were full of the Bible which he had learned as a boy in a closed room by torch light.

Juan Tamad and the Lights

(Juan Tamad is a legendary character of the Philippines. He is the last word in laziness and stupidity. The following story is not authentic folklore, but it resembles the stories that cling to the name of Juan Tamad.)

ONE DAY JUAN TAMAD TIED HIS CARABAO UNDER HIS NIPA HUT, said good-by to his pig and rooster, and started walking off between the rice fields. He had three pesos in his pocket, all his own money. He walked and he walked till he came to the little road leading to the next barrio. Then he walked and he walked till he came to the big highway where the buses ran. Then he rode and he rode till he came to the great city where he had never been before. Then he stared and he stared at all the things that were new and strange to him.

He stared at the cars that seemed to be trying to bump each other off the streets. He stared at the great ships lying at anchor in the bay. He stared at the tall buildings, and the policemen, and the high-heeled shoes of the ladies. He wandered through the markets trying to decide what wonderful things he would buy with a peso to take home to his faraway barrio.

He was still staring and wandering when the sun went down. Of course Juan Tamad expected to see the city people light their candles, but they did nothing of the sort. They simply pushed little buttons attached to glass bulbs and suddenly there was light.

Now Juan Tamad knew what he would buy with his peso—one of those little glass bulbs that made light. He bought a socket to put it in, too, because of course he had to have the button to push. And he bought the wire to hang it from the rafters of his nipa hut. Then Juan Tamad rolled up on an empty table in the deserted market place to sleep contentedly till morning.

The next day he was very careful how he climbed on the bus. He must not hurt that little glass bulb that was going to surprise everyone in his barrio with its magical light. He was very careful how he climbed out of the bus. But as he walked along the barrio road, he was not careful any more. To right and left he shouted, "Come to my house tonight as soon as it is dark. I have a surprise to show you. I brought it from the city."

Juan Tamad walked between the rice fields to his own nipa hut. He untied his carabao, said good morning to his rooster and his pig, and climbed up the ladder to find the best place to hang the wonderful glass bulb. He tied it around one of the rafters so that it hung down in exactly the middle of the nipa hut.

Then he went out again to see his friends. He wanted to be sure everyone would come to his house that night for the surprise.

Before it was dark that night, the barrio friends of Juan Tamad began to arrive. They climbed up the bamboo ladder and crowded into his nipa hut till it swayed and groaned with their weight. They looked about hopefully. They wondered whether the surprise would be to eat or to drink. They could smell nothing cooking. They could hear no dishes clinking. They waited. Some of them lighted candles that they carried with them.

Finally it was really dark, except for the few flickers of candles. Juan Tamad walked to the center of the room. He felt that he should make a speech, but he was not very good at speeches. He cleared his throat and said, "Now! Watch for the surprise!" He pushed the button on the socket of the glass bulb tied to the center rafter of his nipa hut. Nothing happened! He twisted the button. Still nothing happened! He pulled it. Still nothing happened!

Then one of the young men began to laugh. He had worked in a big town. He knew all about little glass bulbs that gave light. "Oh, Juan Tamad," he said, "you can never get an electric light without electric power. One little bulb by itself is not any good. It has to be connected with the power line. You can't have light of your own unless you are connected with the power that gives light."

Then Juan Tamad, feeling very small, lighted his candle so that his barrio friends could find their way down his ladder.

Because he was not at all smart, Juan Tamad probably learned nothing at all from this experience. But, because you are very smart, you can remember that the small lights of our lives are of no use unless they are connected with the Great Power that made the world. And you can remember that there is a straight line to connect your little lights with that Great Power—prayer.

STORIES OF NEGRO SPIRITUALS

Children love to sing the old Negro folk songs. This group of stories may help boys and girls understand the spirituals better as they learn how these songs grew and what they meant to their creators.

"In-a My Heart"

THIS STORY HAPPENED AT ABOUT THE TIME AND PLACE THAT young George Washington was leading an army of his neighbors to defend their homes during the French and Indian War. It happened in the old Colony of Virginia about the year 1756.

A young man named Samuel Davies had come to Hanover, Virginia, from the neighboring colony of Pennsylvania to be a minister to the dissenters. Dissenters were Christians who did not belong to the Church of England, the church of the rulers of the Virginia colony. Some of these dissenters had been put in prison for holding their own services of worship. When Samuel Davies arrived in Virginia, he had to spend many days getting a license from the officials of the colony before he could preach. (He happened to be a Presbyterian, but he would have been called a dissenter also if he had been a Methodist, a Baptist, a Congregationalist, or a Quaker.)

Soon after coming to Virginia, Samuel Davies began preaching services in seven different houses of worship. These were scattered far and wide about Hanover. His congregations included some persons in addition to the white ones who had called him to be their minister. In one section of each church he saw eager dark faces that watched and listened. The slaves were hearing the good news for the first time.

Some of these Negro slaves had come from Africa. Others had been born in this new land, of parents who had been captured as slaves in Africa. They had brought with them their African religion, but it was not full of hope like the religion Samuel Davies preached. They had brought with them their African songs, but they liked also to sing the new church songs. They liked to sing about a God who loved them, about their King Jesus who was their friend, about a land called heaven where they would at last find freedom.

They loved the Bible stories. Moses begged old Pharaoh, "Let my people go!" Joshua fought the battle of Jericho till the walls came tumbling down. Little David played on his harp and grew up to be a great fighter. Daniel was delivered from the lions' den. The troubles of these old-time Bible people reminded the slaves of their own troubles. They liked to hear how God led the children of Israel through dangerous adventures. Perhaps that same God could help Negroes who had been snatched away from their beloved Africa to work in a strange land.

This new religion, called Christianity, gave them hope. And so Samuel Davies found himself preaching the good news to dark, eager faces in each of his seven churches.

Between church services he used to visit these slaves on the plantations where they worked. He talked with them about what it meant to be a Christian—what it meant to be more loving—what it meant to be like Jesus. After their long days of work, they would come to him with questions.

He noticed their love for music. He saw how they sang in time to their work. Sometimes they sang old songs of Africa. Sometimes they sang new songs made up about their new work in the new land. He saw that when they were sad they sang songs about their troubles. He saw that when they were jolly they made up gay songs about their fun. And he knew how they loved the music in their church services.

So Samuel Davies wrote to friends in England about the Negroes' singing and about their wish to become Christians. These friends in England, members of the Society for Promoting Christian Knowledge, sent him books for his Negro friends. Although the slaves had no schools, some of them were eager to read. They managed in one way or another to learn.

For instance, one man who became a famous singer wrote about his mother. When she was a little slave girl, she used to buy reading lessons from the white boy in the big house by giving him a cooky to teach her what he learned in school each day. The slaves who were learning to read welcomed the books from England. They liked all the books. Best of all they liked the books of Christian songs. These were psalms set to music by Isaac Watts.

In writing to his English friends to thank them for the books, Samuel Davies told how the slaves would come to his kitchen in the evening to see the books and then stay far into the night, singing. He would go to bed and wake up hearing them still singing in his kitchen.

In Hanover, just as everywhere that the Negroes heard of the Christian religion, the slaves liked the white folks' hymns, but this music was not quite their own. There was something within them that could make songs to express their new religion in a way that was all their own. And so, in Hanover, and in other towns and plantations, the slaves put together their new religion and their own melodies and rhythms to make some of the sweetest Christian music the world has ever known. In these songs—spirituals we call them—they sang their new faith in their own way. They repeated the Bible stories. They rejoiced in knowing King Jesus. They told their troubles to God. They dreamed about the promised land called heaven.

One spiritual that boys and girls like to sing today is said to have been sung first by the Negro slaves who went to Samuel Davies' churches. In one of his letters to his friends in England, Samuel Davies wrote of the slaves who came to him to talk about becoming Christians. He said there were many, but he told of one in particular. This slave came to him with a question in "broken English" which Samuel Davies repeats in plain English:

"I am a poor slave, brought into a strange country, where I never expect to enjoy liberty," said the man. "While I lived in my own country, I knew nothing of that Jesus which I have heard you speak so much about. I lived quite careless of what would become of me when I died, but I now see that such a life will never do; and I come to you, sir, that you may tell me some good things concerning Jesus Christ, and my duty to God; for I am resolved not to live any more as I have done."

That was a long way of saying: "I want to be a Christian in my heart. I want to be more loving in my heart. I want to be like Jesus in my heart."

Nobody knows the name of the Negro slave who first sang this spiritual. Nobody knows how many Negro singers added to it until it grew to be the song we have today. But those who have studied the growth of Negro music feel quite certain that the song "I want to be a Christian in-a my heart" was sung first by the slaves who came to Samuel Davies and told him that they wanted to be Christians.

REFERENCES: *Sketches of Virginia* by William Henry Foote (1850); and *Negro Slave Songs in the United States* by Miles Mark Fisher (New York: Cornell University Press, 1953).

"Steal Away"

ON STATE HIGHWAY 58 IN VIRGINIA, THERE IS AN IRON MARKER which tells about a Negro slave named Nat Turner. Strangely, this marker tells only of his part in an unhappy incident in 1831 that would be better forgotten. It does not tell how Nat Turner made up a song that is loved today by both colored and white people wherever Christian songs are sung.

Very few Negro spirituals have come down to us with the name of the person who sang them first. Most of the songs just seemed to grow when a group of Negroes were together. One would sing a bit. Then another would add something. Then someone else would sing another line or two. They would repeat the song, with changes, until the words and the melody pleased them.

There were, however, a few Negro musicians in those days who stood out because of their special talents. We have the names and the stories of a few old-time slaves who led the others in their spirituals. The leaders would sing out the lines to which the others sang the answers. And we have the names and stories of a few old-time Negroes who made up songs to tell what they were thinking and what was happening around them.

Nat Turner was one of these slaves who were known as the makers of new spirituals. He had a sweet, strong voice which he used for preaching as well as for singing. Nat Turner had dreams and he believed them. He thought he saw visions of himself leading his fellow slaves to freedom. He thought he heard voices that told him to fight for freedom for himself and for all slaves. In his dreams he heard God calling him by the thunder. He heard God calling him by the lightning. He heard a trumpet sound within his soul which told him he must seek freedom for the slaves who trusted him as their preacher and their leader.

The slaves had brought with them from their homeland the old African custom of secret meeting. In the early days in America, they used to meet secretly in the wilderness for the songs and the dances of their old African religion. When they became Christians, they liked to steal away quietly by themselves for Christian worship. These secret meetings were useful also when they had plans to discuss.

So, when Nat Turner thought he saw visions and heard voices, he wanted to share them with the other slaves. The African custom of the secret meeting gave him his chance. The times were early mornings while the white masters slept, or evenings after the work was done, or Sundays when the slaves rested from their work. In earlier days, the beat of a drum, African-style, called the slaves together. By Nat Turner's time (1800-31), the white masters had ruled: "No drums to call meetings." The slaves had to think of another way to send word from cabin to cabin that there would be a secret meeting at the chosen spot in the wilderness. They knew that their white masters were so used to their singing that they would pay little attention to their songs. All they needed were songs that sounded like one thing to the white masters but had a hidden message for each other.

Among the spirituals there are several that were first used in this way. The one that stands out for its beauty is the one that is believed to have been made up by the singer, Nat Turner. It was sung with two meanings—a religious call to steal away to Jesus and a hidden call to steal away to a secret meeting.

This song was so beautiful that it lived as one of the favorite spirituals after it was no longer needed for its hidden meaning. You have probably sung it yourself. It is in the hymnbooks used in many church schools. Have you guessed which spiritual it is?

Steal away, steal away, steal away to Jesus;
Steal away, steal away home.
I ain't got long to stay here.

My Lord calls me,
He calls me by the thunder;
The trumpet sounds within-a my soul!
I ain't got long to stay here.

My Lord calls me,
He calls me by the lightning;
The trumpet sounds within-a my soul!
I ain't got long to stay here.

The song no longer refers to the voices that came like thunder, like lightning, like trumpets to Nat Turner. It no longer calls anyone to steal away in early morning or late evening to a secret meeting in the wilderness. It now has only its religious meaning—the call to think of Jesus, to listen to the words that he puts in our hearts, to love and follow him.

REFERENCES: *The Confessions of Nat Turner, Leader of the Late Insurrection in Southampton, Va.* (1831); and *Negro Slave Songs in the United States* by Miles Mark Fisher (New York: Cornell University Press, 1953).

"Go Down, Moses"

INDIAN FIGHTER? HUNTER? EXPLORER? MISSIONARY? SCIENTIST? What sort of man on horseback can you guess would write such entries in his journal as these?

Virginia. Monday, April 5, 1790. We made an early move. After worming the stream for a while, we took through the Laurel Hill, and had to scale the mountains, which in some places were rising like the roof of a house. . . . We slept at the Beaver Dam in a cabin without a cover, except what a few boards supplied: we had very heavy thunder and lightning, and most hideous yelling of wolves around; with rain, which is frequent in the mountains.

Tennessee. Tuesday, April 6, 1790. We were compelled to ride through the rain, and crossed the Stone Mountain: those who wish to know how rough it is may tread in our path. What made it worse to me was, that while I was looking to see what was become of our guide, I was carried off with full force against a tree that hung across the road . . . , and my head received a very great jar, which, however, was lessened by my having on a hat that was strong in the crown. We came on to the dismal place called Roan's Creek, which was pretty full. Here we took a good breakfast on our tea, bacon, and bread. Reaching Watauga, we had to swim our horses, and ourselves to cross in a canoe; up the Iron Mountain we ascended, where we had many a seat to rest, and many a weary step to climb. At length we came to Greer's, and halted for the night.

Wednesday, April 7, 1790. We reached Nelson's chapel about one o'clock, after riding about eighteen miles. Now it is that we must prepare for danger, in going through the wilderness.

So the journal goes on. Its writer crosses swollen streams on swimming horses, on ferries, in canoes. When he passes places where the Indians have been fighting the settlers, he steps quietly: the same Indians may be watching him. He rides eighteen or thirty miles a day. He rides three hundred miles a fortnight. Some of the time he is so sick that he cannot stay in the saddle but must find a cabin where he may rest. He rides through snow and sleet in the winter. He rides through rain, gnats, and mosquitoes in the summer. He sleeps wherever he can at night, sometimes under the open sky, sometimes in front of the fireplace in a mud-floored mountain cabin, and sometimes in the town homes of friends. He is loved by many. He is jeered and threatened by others because they do not like the truths he tells. He has no home of his own and no family waiting for him at the end of long travels. He stops a night or a few days in a place and then rides on, back and forth through all the states of the eastern seaboard from Georgia to Maine.

You will know this man as Bishop Francis Asbury, the man who did more than any other to establish the Methodist Church in America. The Negro slaves listened to him as he went up and down the southern states preaching a religion that was new to them. And they gave him a new nickname.

The Africans, as Bishop Asbury calls the Negro slaves in his journal, loved a good story. There is no better book of stories than the Bible. They loved stories about Abraham, Jacob,

Gideon, Joshua, David, Daniel, and Ezekiel. Especially they liked to hear the stories about Moses. When they heard about the children of Israel working as slaves in a foreign land, they were reminded of themselves working as slaves far from their homeland, Africa. When they heard about Moses pleading with King Pharaoh, "Let my people go!" they liked to think that someday they would have a Moses to plead with their masters, "Let my people go!" They dreamed that someday their own Moses would lead them to their promised land—their homeland of Africa or heaven, the land of their religion.

As Bishop Asbury came over and over again to their churches and their plantations, he showed that he cared about his friends whom he called Africans. They knew that he was talking with their masters about giving them freedom. They knew that he had persuaded the ministers he visited to free their slaves. They knew that he gave freely of his time to talk with them. Because they had to work during the daytime, six days a week, he used to meet them early in the morning while their white masters slept. In those early morning services he prayed and sang with them and told them the stories of their new faith.

Bishop Asbury welcomed the slaves into the church services with their white masters on Sundays or in the evenings when their work was finished. He invited them into the houses where he was staying. He went to their cabins to see them. Here was a white man who truly loved them. He never suggested their rising against their masters nor disobeying their masters. In quiet ways he showed the Negroes that he loved them and hoped for the day when they would be free. He wanted this freedom to come because their masters would want them to be free. That was why they thought up the nickname for him.

In the journal, Bishop Asbury often wrote that the Africans felt their religion deeply. Sometimes he was discouraged about the white people's religion, but always he praised the Negroes for their enthusiasm and for their eagerness to learn. The slaves felt his love and respect. They gave him the nickname that was the highest praise they could give any person. It was a name that other slaves in other places gave to men or women who were good to them—Moses.

When the Negroes liked a Bible story, they were likely to sing it rather than tell it. They made the story of Moses into a song. And as they sang about Moses, they thought of the first Moses begging Pharaoh to let his people go. They thought also about their own "Moses," Bishop Asbury, who loved them enough that he wanted freedom and Christianity for them. The song about Moses grew gradually as most Negro spirituals grew, a line at a time, a stanza at a time. On one plantation it would be sung one way. On another plantation it would be sung another way. Today, we sing three stanzas beginning:

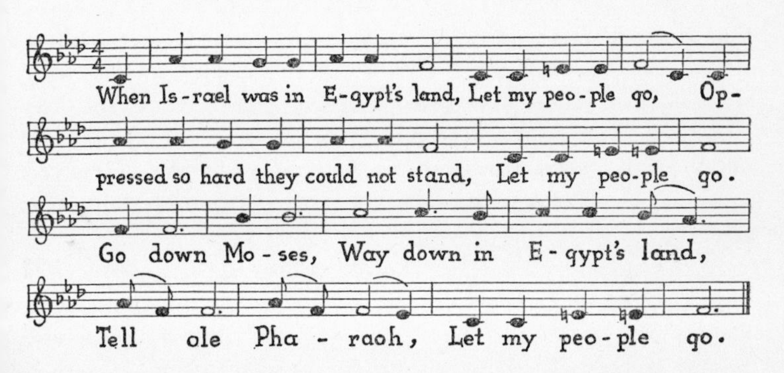

In the old collection the song has twenty-five stanzas. Two have a special story about them. At first the white and colored people attended the same church services. But, as Francis Asbury had reported in his journal, the Africans were much more enthusiastic about their religion than their white masters were. They had brought with them from Africa a way of worshiping that they transferred to their new religion. When they felt happy about their religion they liked to shout and jump. They liked to sing loud while they clapped their hands and stamped their feet in time to their music. The white masters sometimes told the slaves to be still or else not come to church.

So much enthusiasm in worship disturbed the white masters.

Bishop Asbury could not persuade some of the white people to put up with the shouting and clapping and jumping of the Africans. He knew it would be wrong to tell the Negroes to be quiet when they worshiped. What he did was to help them start their own churches where they could worship as they pleased. Their churches were part of his Methodist family.

Their chance to worship in their own way made the Negroes still more grateful to Francis Asbury. So they added two new verses to their Moses song:

I'll tell you what I like the best,
Let my people go.
It is the shouting Methodist,
Let my people go.

Refrain: Go down, Moses . . .

I do believe without a doubt,
Let my people go.
That a Christian has the right to shout,
Let my people go.

Refrain: Go down, Moses . . .

River Songs

IN HIS JOURNAL FOR JANUARY 4, 1790, BISHOP FRANCIS ASBURY wrote: "We crossed James River, with a fresh wind ahead, and only two poor blacks, where four ferrymen are necessary. Two brigs undersail came down full upon us, and we had hard work to get out of their way. These large ferries are dangerous and expensive: our [ferries] alone have cost us three pounds since we left Annapolis."

On this crossing those two slaves were straining every muscle to do the rowing of four men, and dodging boats that threatened to run them down. Possibly on that crossing, they were too busy to sing as they rowed. Bishop Asbury had plenty of chances, however, to hear the ferrymen sing at their oars. Nearly every page in his journal reporting his missionary trips through the southern states mentions a river crossing or a trip by ferry on one of the rivers. While the slaves rowed or poled the boats, they sang songs that kept time with the rhythmic movements of their arms and backs.

There were quick songs for light loads rowed with the current, such as the verses beginning:

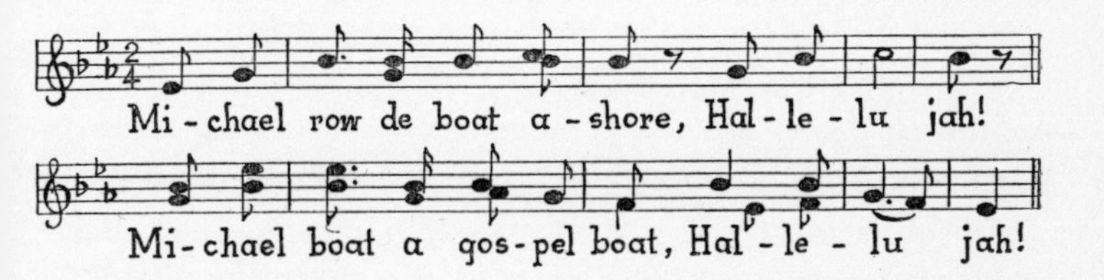

There were slow tunes for heavy loads rowed against the tide, such as the one of sixteen stanzas, beginning:

These songs were often not about rowing on the river. Some were the same songs that were sung in a different way at praise meetings or at the "shout" that might follow one of those meetings.

"Where do your songs come from?" a Civil War colonel once asked a strong young oarsman on a ferry. He had asked this question many times without any good answer. This time he asked the right person.

"Some good spirituals are started jest out o' curiosity," the oarsman answered. "I been a-raise a sing myself once."

Then, because the colonel waited to hear more, the oarsman told how a song had come into his mind once when he was toting rice. Something he said and something another man said made him think of it. Then he "made a sing, jest puttin' a word, and den anudder word."

To show what he meant, the young man started singing. The oarsmen and other workers on the ferry had never heard that "sing" before. But they listened as they worked. Soon they were all singing with him. And, likely as not, they would change his "sing" as they went along and add new lines to it. They would sing it at night with their friends outside their cabins till it grew to be everybody's "sing."

An old book published soon after the slaves were freed, *Slave Songs of the United States* (1867), gives some of the songs that were most often sung by the men who rowed the river boats. Here are just a few of them. Notice how they repeat what Francis Asbury and the other preacher had been teaching about Christianity, a religion that was new to them. Notice how the songs might swing along in time to the pulling of oars, two measures to each stroke.

One song grew from Jesus' parable:

> Every one then who hears these words of mine and does them will be like a wise man who built his house upon the rock; and the rain fell, and the floods came, and the winds blew and beat upon that house, but it did not fall, because it had been founded on the rock. And every one who hears these words of mine and does not do them will be like a foolish man who built his house upon the sand; and the rain fell, and the floods came, and the winds blew and beat against that house, and it fell; and great was the fall of it. (Matt. 7:24-27.)

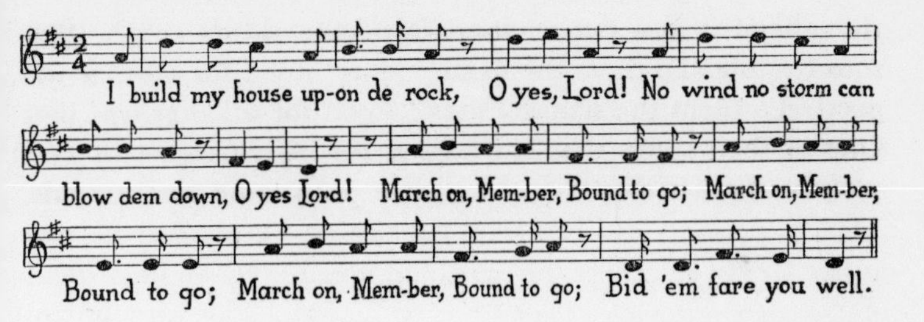

Another song shows that the singers had been hearing the stories of Jesus who went around doing good. You can find New Testament stories to fit the first five stanzas, but do not try to find the iron-gray horse and the milk-white horse in the Bible. Because the Christian religion was new to them, the Negro song makers sometimes added details to the Bible stories.

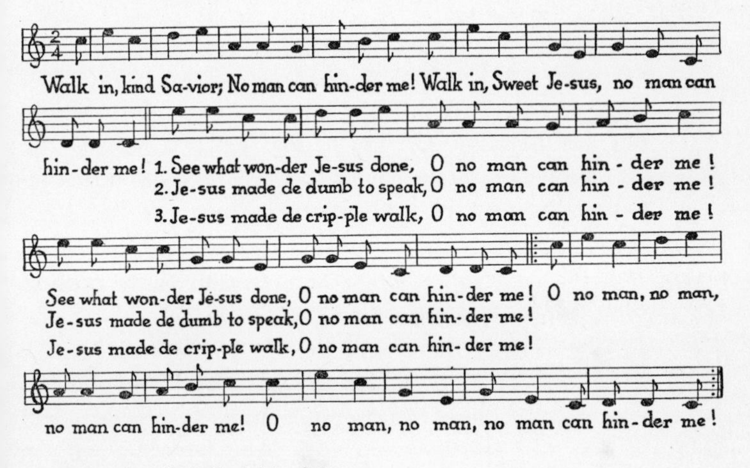

4. Jesus give de blind his sight . . .
5. Jesus do most anyt'ing . . .
6. Satan ride an iron-gray horse . . .
7. King Jesus ride a milk-white horse . . .

The singers, you see, had a name for the temptation to do wrong—Satan. They could fight wrong better if they thought of it as a person that was trying always to get them into trouble. To them the name "Jesus" stood for all that was good. To them the name "Satan" stood for all that was bad. One of their songs that has a good rowing rhythm tells very plainly whether they choose Satan or Jesus to be on their side.

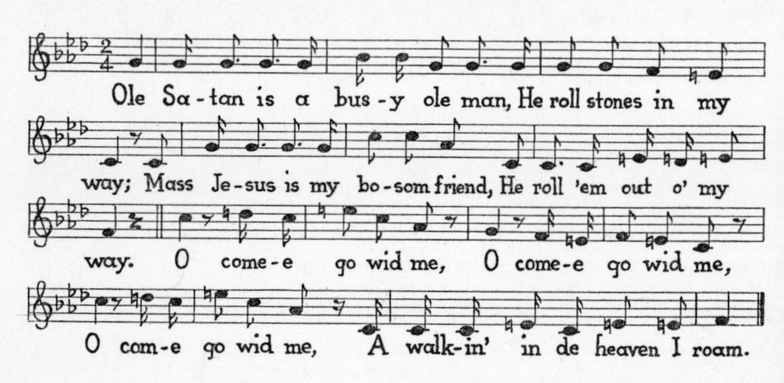

"The Beam in My Sister's Eye"

NERGO SPIRITUALS HAD BEEN SUNG MANY TIMES BY MANY PERSONS before their words and tunes were caught on paper. Those who wrote these songs down could tell where and when they themselves first heard them. Usually, however, they could not tell who sang the spirituals first nor how many people had added bits to them.

The story that follows is made up to show how the Negro spirituals were born. It is not really a true story, but it might have happened. The song in this story is one that was old when *Slave Songs of the United States* was published in 1867.

The workday was over. The men had come back to their cabins after their long hours of work in the cotton fields. The women had come back from their work in the fields, in the big house, or in the cook house and laundry that stood behind the big house. The men were talking, laughing, and singing together. The children were playing or were being tucked into bed. The women were working in their own little cabins.

This was the time of day when Preacher John walked among the cabins talking to the people. He had worked in the cotton fields with the other slaves, but evenings and Sundays he was their preacher, and they loved him.

"We missed you at praise meeting yesterday," he said to a man who was tinkling a banjo in his doorway.

"I came to see your new child," he said to a woman who was cuddling a tiny baby in a patched blanket.

"I'm glad to hear you making music, Sister Rosy," he said to an unsmiling woman who was humming as she swept the hard dirt around her cabin door. "That's a good song, 'Are You Sure the News Is True?' I'm glad you keep your doorstep just as clean as your cabin."

"I *always* sing the praise tunes, and I *always* keep things clean." Sister Rosy stopped her sweeping to look sternly at the preacher. "I'm not like Sister Katy."

"Sister Katy?" Preacher John was surprised to hear such scorn in Rosy's voice. "Sister Katy's a good woman."

"Good!" snorted Sister Rosy. "She lets her cabin go dirty while she plays with her children. Just a-playing and a-laughing and a-singing silly little tunes. Is that what you call being a good woman?"

"But Sister Katy's children are happy all the time." Preacher John looked at Sister Rosy's solemn children. They were not playing. They were just standing, looking at him. "It's good to make children happy."

"It's bad to have dirt around the cabin door." Sister Rosy started swinging her broom again. She was through talking to the preacher, but he was not through talking with her.

"You remind me of something in the Bible. You remind me of something Jesus said." He found himself talking not only to Sister Rosy but to the women of the neighboring cabins also.

They had overheard. They crowded about wondering what Preacher John would have to say about Sister Katy who played with her children even though there was litter about her cabin door.

"Massa Jesus says it is wrong to see the mote in our brother's eye, or in our sister's eye, and not see the beam in our own eye." Preacher John saw that the women did not understand, so he explained. "Massa Jesus liked to laugh. He liked to make people laugh. So he talked about a man going about with a great big piece of wood sticking out of his own eye, but not even noticing it was there. All that man could see was the tiny speck of dust in his brother's eye. And Massa Jesus says that doesn't make sense. It's good to keep your own door clean, Sister Rosy, but you better look for the bad things you do. You better leave your sister's door for her to take care of."

Then Preacher John walked on between the cabins. The tune that Sister Rosy had been humming was still in the minds of the women. So were Preacher John's words.

"You'd better lef' your sister's door," sang one of the women to a tune that was like, but not exactly like, the tune Sister Rosy had been humming.

"Go keep your own door clean," sang another of the women, changing just a little the tune they had been hearing.

Then together the two women sang the two lines:

> You'd better lef' your sister's door.
> Go keep your own door clean.

Sister Rosy had been thinking about what Preacher John had said. She remembered that Sister Katy was kinder and more friendly than she herself had ever been. Sister Katy was a good neighbor to anyone who was sick or in trouble. She, Rosy, never had time to help other people because she was so busy keeping her own cabin and dooryard in order. Maybe there had been a beam in her own eye all this time while she had been talking about Katy's faults. By this time she had forgotten the exact words Preacher John had said that Massa Jesus used. But she remembered the general idea.

So when the other women stopped singing their two lines, she sang two of her own:

> I saw de beam in my sister's eye,
> Can't saw de beam in mine.

The neighbors liked her song, and added it to theirs. When Preacher John walked back between the cabins he found the women swaying and clapping hands in time to the new song.

"That's a good song," praised Preacher John. "Sing it at the praise meeting tomorrow evening."

When the women sang their new song at the next praise meeting, the men liked it so well that someone added a line, and someone added another, and another, and another. And a new spiritual had been created.

STORIES FOR SPECIAL OCCASIONS

The stories of this group are not limited to the days suggested for their telling. Other stories are appropriate for special days, such as "The Eternal Flame of the Cherokees" for Brotherhood Sunday, "The Hidden Treasure" for Bible Sunday, or "The Tears of the Yunwi Tsunsdi" for Good Friday.

A Refugee Gives Thanks

Lincoln's Birthday or One Great Hour of Sharing

JOSEF REZNAK WAS HAPPY, AND VERY GRATEFUL. HE WANTED to say "Thank you" for all the good things that he had found in his new country.

He was free. He was not afraid. He could go to church and worship God with friends who were glad to welcome him. He and his wife had good positions as domestic workers in a family that paid them regular wages in good American money. His family had a comfortable home with plenty of good food. His daughter could go to high school with boys and girls who had always been free, and fed, and unafraid. Moreover, there was a school where Josef Reznak and his wife could go, evenings, when their work was finished.

At this night school, they were learning English—even how to read it and write it. They were also learning the story of their great new country. They were learning how it was founded by brave men from other lands—how it won its freedom and independence—how it gave freedom to dark-skinned people who were once slaves—how people whose ancestors came from many lands were working together to make the country better—how America was trying to help other lands to find freedom. In this same night school, they learned about American heroes—George Washington, Thomas Jefferson, Abraham Lincoln, and many others. Josef Reznak was proud of his new country. He was grateful to the people who had made this country what it is, and to the people who had brought him here to share in its good things. He wanted to say "Thank you."

Some men, if they had been in Josef Reznak's place, might have envied their neighbors and been sorry for themselves. Josef could have pitied himself for the terrible years he had spent in Czechoslovakia during World War II. He could have complained because he and his family had been driven from their home and their business. He could have been thinking of the crowded refugee camps where they had lived with thousands of other refugees. He could have thought how he had suffered in comparison with his neighbors who lived in the comfortable houses of Great Neck on Long Island.

But Josef was happy, and he was grateful. His hard years during the war had taught him what it is to be afraid, and hungry, and crowded, and a slave. That was why he wanted to say "Thank you" for his freedom and his family's chances to earn and to learn. He must find a special way to show how he felt about his new life.

What he learned at night school gave him his idea. As he studied the history of the United States, one man meant America for him. This hero had understood freedom and had tried to spread that freedom until it included every person in the country. This man had the courage to do hard things. He had the wisdom to make right choices. He had the great heart that made him love and understand common people. He could tell funny stories that made people think, or he could say great words, such as ". . . with malice toward none; with charity for all; with firmness in the right, as God gives us to see the right." To Josef Reznak, Abraham Lincoln meant America. Josef wished he could share with everyone who went to his school—in daytime as well as in the evening—his feeling about the great man who stood for freedom and the chance for a good life.

Luckily, Josef Reznak had a talent. He knew a way he could use his skillful hands to thank the school that had been teaching him what it means to be an American.

First, he studied pictures of Abraham Lincoln till he knew every line of the homely, kindly face. Next he bought a big block of pure white plaster. Then he took his sharp sculpturing tools and went to work. He carved slowly and carefully. His bust of Abraham Lincoln must show the great kindness and the great wisdom of his hero. His daily work left Mr. Reznak but little time to carve. It was months before his statue was finished.

Josef Reznak's "Thank you" was ready.

The eight hundred boys and girls of the junior high school met in their assembly hall one morning in April of 1954. They saw, standing on the platform with the rector and their principal, the man from Czechoslovakia, a servant in one of the homes of their town. He was standing before the heavy stage curtains.

He spoke to the boys and girls, slowly, in the English he had learned at night school in their own building. He told them what it meant to him to be an American. He told them his belief that Abraham Lincoln stood for the best in America. He told them that he wanted to say "Thank you" for what his new country and their school had done for him.

Then the curtains were pulled apart—and there was the bust of Abraham Lincoln. It looked so much like the great American that it was hard to believe the bust was modeled by a man who spent his time in a kitchen rather than in a studio.

Giving thanks once was not enough for Josef Reznak. He

had thanked the school which had taught him about Abraham Lincoln and about America. Now he wanted to thank Church World Service, the organization that helped him leave the refugee camps and come to this land where he could work, and worship, and live in peace. And so he started to model a bust of Harper Sibley, the chairman of Church World Service. A year and a half after he had thanked the school, the second statue was given to Church World Service, the great organization through which the churches work together to help the unfortunate people of the world.

Now anyone who goes into the offices of Church World Service can see this statue of Harper Sibley. It shows how one refugee said "Thank you" to the country that gave him a new chance and to the Christian people who made it possible for him to come to the new country.

Each One Bring One

Race Relations or Home Missions

"COPOLAMELO!" SHOUTED MOSE. HIS FRIENDS LAUGHED TILL THEY almost rolled in the dust of the farm labor camp near Pompano, Florida. The boys who were not Mose's friends glared, and muttered to each other in their own Spanish, the language Mose was mimicking.

"Loconamula!" shouted Jeff. It seemed funny to the colored boys, but not to Manuelo and Juan, the Puerto Ricans whose talk he was ridiculing.

Manuelo picked up a stone. He weighed it in his hand ready to throw it. Then he sized up the crowd of laughing boys. They were too many. He dropped the stone and muttered in Spanish to Juan. The two walked past the laughing boys, chins in the air.

Jeering till Manuelo and Juan were out of sight behind one of the little houses that stood in rows, Mose and his friends suddenly felt someone watching them. The green station wagon labeled "The Harvester" had stopped nearby.

"Oh, Mr. Preacher," Mose greeted the man at the wheel. "We just having fun. We like to make up Puerto Rican jabber."

The preached looked at them but said nothing.

"Sure they don't like it." Pete realized what the man in the station wagon was thinking. "That not our fault. Those crazy-talking folks got no right coming to our camp. Let 'em pick tomatoes back where they come from. This place for colored folks."

The preacher said nothing, though his face showed what he was thinking. The boys tried new excuses.

"It's more'n their talk," said Charlie. "They're queer other ways. They sing with a guitar—sort of whiney-dreamy—not bouncey-dancey with a banjo like us."

Mose took his turn. "They dress funny. Some little kids don't dress at all. Our ma's and pa's don't like that."

"They eat funny," Pete added. "Rice and beans—rice and beans—rice and beans. Why don't they eat collards, and fried fish, and hush puppies like regular folks?"

Finally the man in the station wagon was ready to speak, but he did not say what the boys expected. Instead of scolding them for mimicking their Spanish-speaking neighbors, he asked, "Are you boys coming to Sunday school tomorrow?"

"Sure, we're coming!" Mose spoke for them all. That was the least they could do after Mr. Preacher had made them ashamed without scolding. Besides, they liked to go to church and Sunday school in the big assembly building. They liked to sing, hear stories, recite Bible verses together, and make things. It was good to be with Mr. Preacher and his pretty young wife.

Mose and his gang were in their places next day when the preacher led the first song. They were ready to listen when he started to talk.

In less than two minutes they knew Mr. Preacher was talking especially to them. They knew, too, that most of the other colored boys and girls in the big camp for migrant workers liked to tease the Puerto Ricans. They knew the Puerto Ricans fought back whenever they dared.

But listen to what Mr. Preacher was saying. He was talking about the Bible verse "Let us love one another." He was saying that "one another" meant more than folks of your own color. It meant white folks too. It meant mixed-color folks like the Puerto Ricans, who were sometimes white and dark in the same family. You didn't stop with loving folks that looked like you, dressed like you, played like you, ate like you, and sang like you. You loved folks that were different from you. Mr. Preacher was saying that other folks weren't queer just because they were different.

"The Puerto Ricans are better than we are in some ways." That made Mose and the others sit at attention. "They are better friends than we are. When you meet your friends, what do you do? You just wave a hand and say 'Hi!' When the Puerto Rican friends meet, what do they do?"

"I know!" A little girl named Maudie raised her hand. "They throw their arms around each other. They're awfully glad to see each other."

Mose nodded, and so did Pete. They knew how the Puerto Ricans stood up for their friends, even to fighting for them.

After the preacher had talked more about being friendly with migrant neighbors who were different from themselves, he made a suggestion that caused all the boys and girls to sit straight in their seats and stare at him.

"We ought to share our church and Sunday school, and

all our games and clubs with them. It doesn't matter who came to the farm labor camp first. They're here now. It's their camp as much as ours." Then he asked the question that made them all gasp, "How many of you promise to bring a Puerto Rican child to church next Sunday?"

The boys and girls stared at the preacher.

"That gives you just one week to make a friend and invite that friend to come here with you." He looked from face to face.

Slowly Maudie raised her hand. Slowly other hands went up from the girls' classes. Then from the boys' side one hand waved. It was Mose's. Soon there were eighty hands in the air. Eighty boys and girls promised to bring a Puerto Rican friend to church in the big assembly hall.

The story of the next week should be told in eighty parts, one part for each child. It was an easier week for some than for others.

Maudie, for instance, began the minute she reached home. There was a Puerto Rican girl just her age living in the other room of her house—Maudie and her parents and two brothers in one room, Carmen and her parents and three sisters in the other room through the thin wall. Maudie knew everything that happened on Carmen's side, but she had never thought of playing with a girl who had straight hair, and pale skin, and a language that sounded like gibberish.

But this Sunday Maudie said "Hi!"

Carmen smiled and said "Hi!"

Then Maudie took from her pocket a red rubber ball and the little pebbles she used for jackstones. She sat on her doorstep and patted the spot beside her. Carmen sat down. Maudie took a turn at jackstones, then passed ball and stones to Carmen. Carmen's quick hands played without a mistake.

As the week passed there were many things the two girls could do together. By Sunday, Maudie and Carmen were walking with their arms around each other when they went to church.

Choosing a Puerto Rican friend was not so easy for some

others, Mose for instance. He had mimicked Spanish so many times—"Laluluso" or "Pocopucupaca"—that he felt foolish trying to be friends. The days when he stayed home from school to pick beans, Mose watched the Puerto Rican boys working in the fields beside him. On the days when he went to school, he stared at the Puerto Rican boys riding in the yellow school bus with him. Evenings, when Mose and his friends were boxing in front of their cabins, he gave quick glances at the Puerto Ricans dancing to guitar music.

Sunday crept nearer. Mose wished he had not raised his hand. Mr. Preacher was such a good fellow. Mose couldn't let him down. Looking for good in Puerto Ricans, Mose found it. Carlos was a fast worker in the bean field. Juan's smile danced. Mingo was smart in arithmetic even though he knew little English. Ricardo was the friend of every dog in camp. But still Mose could not make himself invite anyone.

Saturday arrived. Seventy-nine of the boys and girls who had raised their hands last Sunday had invited their guests for church. Still Mose had not found anyone to ask when he went to the store to buy bread for his mother. His little sister, Susie May, tagged after him.

"Keep an eye on Susie May," his mother yelled.

"Yes'm." Mose was not thinking.

The migrants had been paid that day for their week's work. There was money to buy gasoline. Those who had old cars were driving them. The twisting roads through the farm labor camp were no place for a tiny girl to tag after a brother who forgot to watch her. Mose walked on, eyes on the ground, figuring how he could keep his promise to the preacher in the few hours left before church tomorrow morning.

There was a screech of brakes behind him, and the squeal of tires stopping fast on hot stones. There were screams of women sitting in the doorways of little houses.

Suddenly Mose remembered Susie May. He wheeled around. He saw people running from all directions toward the place where the car had stopped. He could not see over the crowded heads.

"Susie May!" he called. There was no answer. There was no toddling girl in a red dress.

"Susie May!" Mose ran toward the crowd as fast as shaky legs would move. He pushed through, not caring how many people he bumped. He must find the truth about his little sister. If anything had happened—

"Hi, Mose!" It was Susie May herself, snuggled in the arms of Juan.

"She all right?" Mose gasped.

"She all right," Juan repeated. "I see car come fast. I grab her from road. Car not touch her. She all right."

Susie May climbed from Juan's arms to Mose's arms, but the two boys walked on together. Mose had trouble finding words big enough to thank Juan. Instead Mose asked, "How would you like to come to church with me tomorrow?"

"Bueno! Good!" Juan smiled his nice dancing smile. It was good to have a friend. Mose thought so too.

Alone?

Family Sunday or Father's Day

AS KEITH GREW OLDER, HIS HOBBIES CHANGED, BUT HIS PRIDE IN doing things by himself did not change until the day his father laughed in the locker room of the high school gymnasium.

One year his hobby was his electric train. Of course his dad bought it and helped him figure out the directions. His mother gave him a corner of the dining room and protected his tracks from Peter the pup and Bert the baby. Keith, however, let it be known that he, and he alone, knew how to run that train.

The next year his hobby was his butterfly collection. Dad came in handy when Keith needed money to buy a net, materials for mounting specimens, or books about butterflies. Mother would call him to see new varieties fluttering above her flower garden, and she would be patient about letting him mess around in her clean kitchen. But Keith was proud to claim all the credit for his cases of butterflies and moths.

The next year Keith joined the 4-H club. Then for several years there was nothing more important than his Holstein calves, a new one each year. Of course the calves came from his dad's herd, grazed in his dad's pasture, and ate grain from his dad's feed bins. When the calves jumped the fence during school hours, there was only his mother to chase them back into the pasture. But when the ribbons were handed out at the calf exhibit of the county fair, Keith puffed up his chest when he thought how he had earned his ribbon singlehanded, by his own hard work.

When Keith was old enough to ride the school bus to high school, his new hobby was wrestling. He was told by the coach that he stood a good chance of making the team if he practiced hard and never broke training.

"Dad," Keith said, "I'll be missing the school bus home every night now because of wrestling practice. I can ride with Mr. King when he comes home after work."

"But he doesn't come home until after 5:30 every night." Dad was thinking about the chores Keith usually did after school. "Who'll drive the cows in from pasture? Who'll help me milk?"

"Isn't Bert old enough to go after the cows alone?" asked Keith. "He ought to be learning to work instead of playing around with my old electric train, or tooting his flute, or hunting snakeskins and stuff for his silly old nature collections."

"Bert isn't old enough to take much responsibility—any more than you did at his age," Dad answered.

"But I have to practice every day," protested Keith. "It's the only way I can make the team."

"Well, wrestling is a good healthy sport," said his father. "I'll manage somehow."

As the wrestling season wore on, the family found that there was more involved than Keith's missing farm work from 4:30 to 5:30 five days a week. Training rules made him go to bed early. Going to bed early meant studying at the time when Keith used to help with evening chores. There was often studying left to do in the morning because Keith must get good marks or he would not be allowed to wrestle.

"At least you can help me on week ends," his father said. But soon Keith was a substitute on the team and had to travel to other schools for Saturday meets. Then he made the first team and it was more important than ever that he miss no meets or practice sessions.

On days that he missed the ride back with Mr. King, he would telephone and his mother would drive to town to bring him home. She hated to spare the time, because meals had become quite a problem since Keith had been in training for wrestling. His food must be very nourishing to give him extra strength, but at the same time it must not put any weight on him. In fact, he had to keep taking off a bit of weight in order to wrestle in the 140-pound class. His mother had to consult the Home Bureau agent and plan new menus and often cook special dishes for Keith. It was a lot of fuss and worry, but she was glad to do it, just as Keith's father was glad to do extra farm work. They wanted their son to succeed in whatever he tried to do.

Finally, Keith's parents had to plan their work so that they could take a Saturday off once in a while to watch a wrestling match. Keith used to tell them: "A fellow can't do his best if his parents don't care enough to see him wrestle."

During one wrestling meet, Keith's dad went to the locker room where the wrestlers were getting ready for their turn on the mat. He thought this was a good time to ask what magic there was in wrestling that made the boys work so hard at it.

"Why do you boys choose wrestling as your favorite sport?" he asked.

The boys all answered at once, and they all said about the same thing. Combining their answers, their reasoning was something like this: "I like wrestling because it puts me on my own. There's nobody working with me. If I lose, it's nobody's fault but mine. If I win, it's nobody's glory but mine. I wrestle alone."

Then Keith's father did something that surprised himself even more than it surprised the boys. He did not mean to do it, but he thought of those boys' fathers. He thought of their mothers. He knew most of them well. Then he could not help doing it. He laughed.

The boys stared at him. "What is funny?"

"I'm sorry," he said. "I did not mean to laugh. But I happen to know what most of your families are doing so that you can build yourselves up as wrestlers. I just had to laugh at your thinking that you are doing it alone. I'm sorry."

At home that evening Keith said nothing about the locker-room incident. His father wondered if the boy was angry. Then he overheard Keith lecturing Bert.

"You should be ashamed of yourself," Keith was telling his little brother. "You brag about how smart you are—taking care of your electric train, or learning to play the flute, or making your nature collections. You say you do it all yourself. Who do you think pays for the new batteries, or flute lessons? Who puts up with all the mess and noise you make? It's time you stopped bragging about doing things alone and said 'thank you' for a change."

Then Keith's father smiled. He knew that all was well.

When the Bible Came Back

Reformation Day or Bible Sunday

MARY PUT HER MOUTH CLOSE TO THE EAR OF HER BROTHER Henry. What she was going to say must be whispered. She did not dare say it aloud.

"I do not want to go to church!" Mary waited to see what terrible thing would happen. The birds still sang, and the crickets still chirped, and the wind still moved the tops of the elm trees of the fourteenth-century English countryside.

"I do not want to go to church either," Henry whispered into her ear, "but we have to go."

Having said the terrible thing, Mary tried to make up for it a little. She could say aloud, "There are a few things I like about church—the colored pictures in the windows—the way the ceiling curves up high—the ringing of the bells in the steeple—the chanting of the choir when the music is not too sad." Mary was talking about the things of the church six hundred years ago that would seem familiar to us today. But both children were thinking of the things that were very different.

"I know what you do not like." Henry lowered his voice. "You do not like the priest. You know he is selfish and lazy all week. How can he be good all of a sudden on Sunday? You don't like the way he is always asking for money—money—money, promising to say prayers for us or for the dead. I don't see why we can't say our own prayers."

"And I don't like his talking in Latin all the time except when he asks for money." Mary was forgetting to whisper. "The Bible chained to the pulpit is so big that there must be something interesting in it. But how can we know if he always reads in Latin?"

"You heard Father say the priest is afraid to let us know what is in the Bible," Henry reminded her. "He says the priest is not living by the Bible, and he does not want us to know it."

There was a laugh and quick footsteps on the path behind the children. They wished they had remembered to keep whispering. They turned to see who had overheard them. It was a young stranger in the clothes of a priest, carrying a big book. Both children crossed themselves as fast as they could. What could they say? How could they explain?

To their amazement the priest was smiling at them. "This morning I shall have listeners who are not afraid to think for themselves. I am glad!"

The children stared at him. Then Henry remembered. "You are taking the place of our priest while he is away?"

"Yes," said the stranger. "You know he has gone on a pilgrimage to Rome. He is taking some relics to be blessed by the Pope. He asked me to take care of his church—because he did not know me very well."

That seemed a queer reason, but Mary and Henry asked no questions. They were glad their own priest did not know the young priest well. They were glad he was coming to their church. They skipped along the path with the new priest. Going to church did not seem stupid and dreary now.

This priest did not look as though he, like their own priest, slept too much, ate too much, drank too much, and thought too little. His eyes smiled. He was as strong and quick-stepping as their father. The children ran to keep up with him.

The children left him when he went to the altar. They sat near their parents, who had reached the church first. They watched him go through the same forms that their old priest went through every Sunday. It was when he began to speak that the surprise came. He spoke in English, even though he was not asking for money. He talked about the great Latin Bible chained to the pulpit. He said it was full of wise sayings, worshipful poetry, stories of brave men and women. He said that its teachings would show God's will to any man, woman, or child. He said the Bible would give the secret of living as Jesus lived.

Mary and Henry wished more than ever that they could read the big book. But what good was wishing? The Bible was chained. And nobody could read Latin anyway except the priests and a few scholars. Even some priests did not know the meaning of the Latin words they chanted so loudly.

Then the time came for the reading of the Bible. The new priest did an amazing thing. He did not open the great chained Bible and start mumbling in Latin. Instead he placed on the pulpit the big book that he had brought with him. He started reading in English, the language of the people.

First he read a poem about the Bible itself:

> Teach me, O Lord, the way of thy statutes;
> and I will keep it to the end.
> Give me understanding, that I may keep thy law
> and observe it with my whole heart.
> Lead me in the path of thy commandments,
> for I delight in it.
> Incline my heart to thy testimonies,
> and not to gain!
>
> . . . .
>
> I will keep thy law continually,
> for ever and ever;
> and I shall walk at liberty,
> for I have sought thy precepts.
> I will also speak of thy testimonies before kings,
> and shall not be put to shame;
> for I find my delight in thy commandments,
> which I love.
> I revere thy commandments, which I love,
> and I will meditate on thy statutes.
>
> *Ps. 119:33-36, 44-48*

Then he read stories from the New Testament—stories of Jesus healing, Jesus teaching, Jesus praying. He tried to stop reading, but the people called for more. It was what they had been hungry to hear. The people sang while his voice rested so he could read again.

Today Mary and Henry did not keep themselves awake by tracing the grain of the timbers of the high ceiling, or studying the pictures of the colored windows, or listening to the cooing of the pigeons in the steeple. The Bible was keeping them awake—wide awake. They were hearing it for the first time in their own language.

Sometimes the priest looked up from his handwritten English Bible to explain something he had read. Many of his beliefs were not what the old priest taught.

"You can pray directly to God," the young priest told them. "I find nothing in the Bible about confessing your sins to a priest, nothing about paying the priest to pray for you, nothing about praying to the saints or the Virgin. Jesus talked directly to God. He wants us to talk with God."

After the service was over, Henry and Mary were with the people who crowded about the young priest to ask questions.

"John Wycliffe is the man who had the Bible translated into English," he told them. "He has trained preachers to tell the people that the Bible is their own. Some of these preachers have never been priests. Others, like myself, are priests who dare to think for themselves. When the bishops hear what we are saying, we will not be priests any longer. But we will go on preaching the open Bible when our priestly robes have been taken from us."

Walking home on the path across the fields, Mary did not need to whisper to Henry. Out loud she could say, "I like to go to church!"

The Boy Who Watched for Melchior

Christmas

JAMSHID TOILED UP THE HILL, THE BUNDLE OF CLEAN WOOD balanced on his head. The boy knew how to sway his body for every uneven spot on the way. Many a time the hot Persian sun had made him wish he might drop his load and lie in the shade of the fig trees by the water pool at the foot of the hill. But the altar fire must never go out.

As he struggled up the hill, he thought of the stories brought by travelers from the southern part of Persia, stories of oil seeping from a rocky crevice to be burned in the eternal fire. How easy to be an altar boy there! Once when he had mentioned this wistfully to his master, Melchior, that wise man had smiled and answered, "He who would join the Magi must not choose the easy way. As a boy you must toil with your body, so that you may be strong to toil with both body and mind later."

Jamshid knew that Melchior had not chosen the easy way when he struck off across the desert on the long journey from which he had not yet returned.

The boy paused as he reached higher ground. Here he could look through a gap between the hills at rolling desert stretching on and on toward the west. He hoped for sight of his master's dromedary coming across the desert.

He saw a moving cloud of dirt, but it was only a dust whirl so common in a dry land. Another puff of white dust traveling slowly in his direction was stirred up by the many sharp hoofs of a flock of sheep and goats, following their shepherd to the pool of water under the six palm trees. Then came a swiftly moving cloud of dust. It was not big enough to be made by a camel, but by a horseman. Jamshid dropped his faggots and ran down the trail to the pool where he knew the rider would stop for water and rest. The boy reached the pool as the rider dismounted.

"What is the news?" Jamshid asked the question always asked of a traveler.

The man shrugged. "Days and days of empty desert—if you can call that news."

"Did you see any Magi riding dromedaries?" It was the question he had asked of every traveler for many weeks.

"No, but I heard about them at caravansaries along the way," answered the man.

"What did you hear?"

"Nothing much," said the man. "It seems they were Magi with a crazy idea that there was a promised king somewhere in the direction of the Great Sea. They were carrying expensive gifts to this unknown king. Men were joking about them all the way from Palestine to Persia. Wise men indeed! I doubt if they will ever find their way back home again."

Angrily Jamshid picked up a stone and threw it into the still pool. If he were bigger, that is what he would do to the man who laughed at Melchior. Then he ran back to his pile of faggots, balanced them again on his head, and started up the hill.

"What's the matter, Jamshid?" called a boy's voice. "I can tell you are angry by the way you walk."

"Oh, Jotham!" Jamshid waited for the Jewish boy, a descendant of the exiles who had stayed in Persia after many had returned to their homeland of Palestine. "I was angry because a traveler made fun of my master."

"Many of our own city laugh at Melchior," said Jotham quietly.

"I know," admitted Jamshid. "I hate to go into the market place. Someone is sure to say that my master went on a foolish errand. They say he may never come home."

"What will you do if he does not come back?" asked Jotham.

"Melchior will come back!" Jamshid spoke so violently

that he almost upset his load of clean barsom wood. "Until he comes, I do what he told me to do. He trusted me to bring fuel for the eternal fire."

"I never quite understood," said Jotham, "why Melchior was sure there was a new leader."

"It was a sign he read in the skies," answered Jamshid. "You know that our religion teaches the struggle between the good and the evil. There is a prophecy about a great leader called Saoshyant the Victorious. He will appear in a country of the East and will found the good kingdom," said Jamshid. "Then the good will conquer the evil forever."

"We have such a prophecy in our religion." Jotham took part of Jamshid's load and balanced it on his own head as the boys climbed on up the hill. "We call our leader the Messiah. He is to be born in Bethlehem of Judea. He will give our people a good kingdom just as your prophecy says Saoshyant will do for you. But why did Melchior think the leader had come now?"

"You know he sits up all night many times watching the stars. He compares their position with the prophecies in the ancient scrolls that he is always studying," said Jamshid.

"I know." Jotham, trudging along behind his friend, was thinking of the faraway look in Melchior's eyes when he was interrupted in his studies.

"He saw a new star of a brightness never seen before. It was the sign he had been waiting for, he and the other Magi." Jamshid plodded up the trail silently before adding, "And so they took their gifts for the new king. They mounted the swiftest dromedaries they could hire and rode off toward the west. They said they would travel in the cool of the night when they could follow the star."

"How long did the new star shine in the sky?" asked Jotham.

"I counted thirteen nights," answered Jamshid. "Then there were a few cloudy nights. On the next clear night it was gone. That was weeks ago. They should be back now, unless they lost their way in the desert."

"Or unless they stayed to serve the new king!" Jotham remembered how his parents longed for that homeland to the west across the desert.

"Melchior will come back to his altar," said Jamshid. "He is teaching his altar boys to be Magi like himself, but he knows we are not ready to take his place. He will come back."

As the days dragged on, Jamshid toiled daily up the hill with fuel for the altar fire. In the daytime he scanned the desert for dust flurries. Sometimes these would be only dust whirls caused by the wind. Sometimes they would announce the coming of a traveler. When the steady pace and huge size of an approaching steed proclaimed it to be a camel, Jamshid would hope for a rider wearing the white pointed cap and white woolen coat of the Magi. But more often than not, the camel proved to be a pack animal plodding along under a heavy load.

In the night Jamshid would lie on his mat on the flat roof of his home listening to sounds in the street. He listened to hoofbeats, hoping to hear the soft padding of a dromedary. He listened to voices, hoping to hear Melchior.

But day after day he felt the growing smiles as men watched him climbing the hill with his clean wood balanced on his head. He had only the friendship of Jotham, the Jewish boy. The two boys alone had faith that Melchior had done a wise thing and would return. He wished he could do something to repay the boy who understood how he felt toward his master. Even the faith of Jamshid was growing faint when one hot day he climbed the hill, balancing his faggots on his steady head. As he neared the altar, he heard voices, many voices full of questions and excitement. He hurried his steps as fast as he could without upsetting his burden.

Then from the voices he heard the one he had been awaiting, the voice of Melchior. In his happiness Jamshid remembered Jotham. It was only a few steps to the part of the city where the Jewish people lived. He laid down his load, the quicker to run for Jotham. Soon he was back on the path, going up the hill with Jotham following him and carrying part of his load. Reaching the hilltop, they found a tired and thin Melchior. His white cap and robe were thick with dust. His silken undergarment was torn and dirty. Around the sun-tanned man stood other men who laughed.

"Well, Melchior, why didn't you bring your king back with you?" asked one.

"So he took your gift and gave you nothing in return?" asked another.

"Will he be pushing Augustus Caesar from the throne of Rome, or will he be wearing the crown of Phraates here in the Parthian empire?" asked a third. At each question the men laughed.

Jamshid pushed through the crowd, with Jotham close behind him. "Melchior, my master, you are back! Did you find Saoshyant?"

"Did you find the Messiah?" asked Jotham.

"I found the king," Melchior spoke to the boys, forgetting the men who laughed.

"Tell us," said the two boys in one voice.

It was to the boys that Melchior spoke. "Our dromedaries went swiftly across the desert, drinking the wind in the cool of the night and sleeping or grazing in the heat of the day. The star went before us to show us the way. We came to Jerusalem, asking, 'Where is he who has been born king of the Jews? For we have seen his star in the East, and have come to worship him.'

"When Herod the king heard this, he was troubled and all Jerusalem with him; and assembling all the chief priests and scribes of the people, he inquired of them where the Christ was to be born. They told him, 'In Bethlehem of Judea, for so it is written by the prophet.' "

Softly, while Melchior paused as though thinking, Jotham repeated the words which every well-trained Jewish boy knew:

> "And you, O Bethlehem, in the land of Judah,
> are by no means least among the rulers of Judah;
> for from you shall come a ruler
> who will govern my people Israel."

There was something in the boy's reverent voice that stilled the laughter of the men. They formed a quiet circle about Melchior. It was one of them who said, "Go on with your story, Melchior, we beg of you."

"Herod summoned us secretly," he said, "to learn from us what time the star appeared. And he sent us to Bethlehem saying, 'Go and search diligently for the child, and when you have found him bring me word, that I too may come and worship him.'

"When we had heard the king, we went our way. And lo, the star which we had seen from our own hilltops went before us, till it came to rest over the place where the child was. When we saw the star we rejoiced exceedingly with great joy.

"And going into the house we saw the child with Mary his mother. And we fell down and worshiped him. Then, opening our treasures, we offered him gifts, gold and frankincense and myrrh. And being warned in a dream not to return to Herod, we departed to our own country by another way."

There was silence except for the crackling of the altar fire. At last one of the men asked, "How did you know that the child was the new king?"

Melchior did not need to answer. In his eyes was the glad light of a man who is sure beyond the shadow of a doubt. Silently the men filed down the trail, wondering. But Jamshid and Jotham stayed with Melchior, beginning to understand.

STORIES WITH TEXTS

An appropriate Bible text can be found for any character-building story, but it may seem an afterthought. In the stories that follow, Bible quotations are integral parts of narrative that would be incomplete without them.

Fun or Delight

"IF WE SET THE ALARM CLOCK, WE CAN BE ON THE ROAD EARLY." Eleanor and James were bending over a road map spread out on the living-room floor. "We might knock off fifty miles or so before Sunday traffic jammed the roads. We'd be at the beach in time for a swim before dinner. We could fish in the afternoon and be home by bedtime."

That sounded like good planning to the children, but Dad came out with one of his old-fashioned remarks. "That seems a long sabbath day's journey to me!"

"What's a sabbath day's journey?" asked Eleanor. "Is that a different name for a Sunday ride?"

"A very different name," agreed Dad.

"It sounds like the Bible," said James. His father nodded.

"Let's see who can find it first." Eleanor ran for their Bibles. James always said that the whole family had a bad case of "look-it-up-itis" and that Eleanor was the worst. If it wasn't the dictionary, it was the encyclopedia, or the atlas, or the Bible concordance that came out whenever there was question.

With a little help from Dad they found in Acts 1:12 that the disciples "returned to Jerusalem from the mount called Olivet, which is near Jerusalem, a sabbath day's journey away." The maps in the back of the Bible made Mt. Olivet look less than a mile from the walls of Jerusalem. Again with the help of Dad, they found in the encyclopedia that "a sabbath day's journey" was the distance that the ancient Jewish laws allowed a person to travel on the seventh day of the week. They found that this distance would compare to seven-eighths of a mile in our measurement.

"Well, I'm surely glad we don't have to obey that old law on our Sundays," said Eleanor.

"Yes," agreed Dad. "The sabbath day's journey would be pretty hard to enforce in these days. Even in Jesus' time, he taught that the old laws about sabbath observance were too rigid. Remember that he helped people on the sabbath even though the Pharisees were watching him, hoping he would break their sabbath laws. Jesus said: 'The sabbath was made for man, not man for the sabbath.' What bothers me, though, is that we modern Americans are getting so far away from old-fashioned sabbath observance that we are in danger of spoiling the best day of the week."

"What do you mean—spoiling?" James looked up from the road map on which they had been planning a dawn-to-bedtime Sunday trip. "You don't expect us to sit around all day twirling our thumbs, do you?"

"Hardly!" Dad laughed at the thought of James sitting still on any day of the week. "But I do think we could find something between the old Sunday full of 'don'ts' and the new Sunday full of rushing around. Your plan for next Sunday, for instance, does not leave any time for doing what the Bible tells us was Jesus' custom on the sabbath day—going to church. Unless we watch out, it won't leave any time to be quiet and let God talk to us through the best in books, nature, music, people, or our own thoughts. Sunday is the day when we are not pushed by work, or school, or the hundreds of details of everyday living. It is the day for us to grow in our understanding of God. It is the day when we have time to take a long breath and look at life and get a fresh start."

"That doesn't sound very exciting." Eleanor was looking reluctantly at the red line on the road map leading to the far-distant beach.

"Anybody can have the sort of fun you are thinking about," said Dad. "It takes a bigger and wiser person to have something that is better than fun and excitement on Sundays."

"What's that?" asked James.

Dad was hunting for something in the Bible. "Here's a poem written by one of the Hebrew prophets, Isaiah. Listen hard because it's not easy reading. See if you can find in this what is better than fun on the seventh day."

The children listened as he read:

> If you turn back your foot from the sabbath,
> from doing your pleasure on my holy day,
> and call the sabbath a delight
> and the holy day of the Lord honorable;
> if you honor it, not going your own ways,
> or seeking your own pleasure, or talking idly;
> then you shall take delight in the Lord.
>
> *Isa. 58:13-14*

Perhaps Dad bore down a bit on the words "take delight in the Lord." Anyway both children noticed those words.

"Is 'taking delight in the Lord' better than fun?" asked James.

"It is," said Dad. "It's something you have to grow into. You learn it bit by bit. But it's something that never leaves you, no matter what your days are like. It's something that spreads out into the busy weekdays if you take time to 'take delight in the Lord' on Sundays."

The next Sunday James and Eleanor got an idea of what their dad had meant when they shared an after-church walk in the woods with him. They walked slowly, stopping to look closely at the wonders of moss, ferns, rocks, and waterfalls. Everywhere in the woods they felt that God was close to them. His nearness made their "sabbath a delight."

Ant-Watching

ARTISTS WHO DRAW COMIC STRIPS CAN SAY MUCH WITH JUST A few pictures and a few words. But there is a book that can say more in fewer words, with no pictures to help. The cartoonist who draws the newspaper strip "Our Bill" needed 114 words and eight pictures to say what one of the wise writers of the Bible said in twelve words and no pictures.

Here is the story told by the cartoonist in his eight pictures.

Bill and his pop felt like a good long walk on a wonderful sunshiny Saturday morning. They thought a nature hike would be much more fun than cleaning the messy yard. In spite of some good advice from Bill's mother, they left the clean-up job and went hiking off into the world of sunshine and pleasure, the world of nature where there were no little jobs for them to do.

First they watched a big yellow and black bee buzzing on a clover blossom, busy with two jobs at the same time—collecting nectar to make honey, and dusting flowers with the pollen she collected on her legs.

Next they watched the ants, forever on the move. Some were carrying loads bigger than themselves. Others were hurrying about on their six nervous legs as though they had important engagements right away. Bill tried to find a single ant standing idle for at least ten seconds, but every one was working hard at something.

Next there was a flutter of yellow wings, a bird with a piece of straw in its mouth. Bill and Pop stood silently to watch.

They saw the bird weave the straw into the nest she was making before flying off for another bit of material for the new treetop home.

Bill and his Pop walked on into the woods to a favorite brook, stepping quietly so they would not disturb any birds or animals that might be there. Two furry brown beavers were hard at work. One was gnawing through the trunk of a small tree with its four long cutting teeth. The other was dragging a leafy branch to hide under water for next winter's eating.

The hard-working beavers—coming after the busy bee, the industrious ants, and the home-building bird—were too much for Bill and Pop. They rolled their eyes at each other in a questioning sort of way.

"A lot o' work going on around here," said Bill.

"Nature makes a fellow feel sort of no-account and lazy," said Pop.

"Let's go!" said Bill. Pop knew where he meant to go and what he meant to do.

Of course, the last of the eight pictures shows Bill and Pop back in their own yard raking and carting, busy as ants or bees or beavers.

The Bible puts in twelve words what Bill and Pop learned. It is in the book of Proverbs, an old collection of wise Hebrew sayings:

> Go to the ant, O sluggard;
> consider her ways, and be wise.
>
> *Prov. 6:6*

The word "sluggard" means lazy person. Put in modern language, the proverb might be: "Watch the ant, lazybones. See how she works—and be wise."

Onesiphorus, a True Friend

THIS IS ABOUT A MAN WITH A LONG NAME AND A SHORT STORY. There are almost as many letters in his name—Onesiphorus—as there are words in his story as told in the Bible (II Tim. 1:15-18).

The four Bible verses about Onesiphorus are in the Second Letter to Timothy. They seem to have been written by the great Christian missionary Paul while he was in prison in Rome.

Paul, as you may remember, had been arrested because neither the Jews nor the Romans liked to have the people excited by his preaching about Jesus. Paul was not behind prison bars, but he was in some rented rooms and was guarded by a Roman soldier. Paul's friends were allowed to visit him.

Some of these friends were loyal to him. They came often to see him. They brought him whatever he needed. They acted as his postman, carrying letters to and fro. They sat and talked with him about their problems and about their Christian faith.

Others were not such loyal friends. While they were visiting Paul, they were looking at the Roman guard and wondering if they were not taking chances of being arrested themselves. Or, as they left Paul's rooms, they would look up and down the street hoping that nobody would notice where they had been. They thought it might not be wise to let their Roman neighbors or the Roman guards know they were friendly with a man who was a prisoner. They knew that Paul might be put to death at any time. They thought it might be better if they did not come to visit him again.

Some of Paul's former friends were so ashamed or so afraid of being connected with the condemned prisoner that they actually turned against him, and pretended to be siding with his enemies. In the Second Letter to Timothy, Paul has been telling sadly about some of these turncoat friends. Then he tells gladly about the man with the long name and the short story—Onesiphorus.

"Many times did that man put fresh heart into me," he wrote. "And he was not in the least ashamed of my being a prisoner in chains. Indeed, when he was in Rome, he went to a great deal of trouble to find me . . . and you well know in how many ways he helped me at Ephesus as well." (1:16-18 Phillips.)

That is all we know about Onesiphorus. But isn't he the kind of man anyone would like for a friend?

Diotrephes

DID YOU EVER HEAR OF A MAN NAMED DIOTREPHES? PROBABLY not. If you should go to your mother or father or church school teacher and ask, "Who was Diotrephes?" the chances are they would not know either. Even if you gave them the clue, "Diotrephes is in the Bible," they would have a hard time remembering who he was or what he did. And no wonder. Diotrephes never did anything famous. So far as we know he never did anything to help anyone.

He matters to us only if we have the good sense to read about him and then say: "I'll never be like Diotrephes!" You see, he had a bad habit that made it hard for him to get along with other people. Though he lived hundreds and hundreds of years ago, when the Christian Church was young and new, his bad habit is one that you or I can easily have today. As you listen about Diotrephes, ask yourself: "Am I like him? Am I even a little bit like him?"

We meet Diotrephes in a letter written by a Christian leader called "The Elder" to a church leader named Gaius. In the

Bible this letter is known as the Third Letter of John. It seems that the Elder was taking care of many of the young churches in Asia Minor. He was a leader among the Christian teachers who traveled among these new churches. He was writing this letter perhaps thirty or forty years after the great Christian missionaries Peter and Paul had been killed for their preaching in Rome. The Church had continued to grow in the towns and cities around the Mediterranean Sea. It grew because there were leaders, like the Elder, who traveled to explain the teachings of Jesus. It grew because there were other leaders, like Gaius, who worked for God in their own communities while doing their daily work. But sometimes the Church had a hard time because there were men like Diotrephes who pretended to be Christians but who did not know how to work with the others.

There are two verses that tell what trouble Diotrephes is making for the church of which Gaius is a leader. In just a few words, the Elder gives us such a clear picture of Diotrephes that we know right away why he cannot get along with others. The Elder describes him as a man "who wants to be head of everything" (III John 9 Phillips). Diotrephes was working for the Church, to be sure, but he wanted everything to be done in his own way. If they had committees in those days, he would have wanted to be chairman of all the committees. And when he called his committees together, he would not have asked the others what they thought. He would have told them what they must do.

According to the Elder's letter to Gaius, Diotrephes carried his wish "to be head of everything" very far. He refused to take suggestions from those who knew more than he did. He said mean and untrue things about the leaders who were more loved and honored than he was. He was impolite to Christians who came from other churches to visit and to teach in his town. Instead of helping these travelers find a place to stay, he told the others in his church not to welcome them.

And he did all of this because of his very bad habit of wantin
"to be head of everything."

Two Boats

JESUS USED TO TELL STORIES TO MAKE PEOPLE THINK. FOR IN
stance, there was the one he told when he noticed some me
who were puffed up with pride in themselves. He saw ho
they were looking down their scornful noses at everyone else
The Bible story describes them as "some who trusted in them
selves that they were righteous and despised others" (Luk
18:9).

If Jesus had been like most of us, he might have told then
that he did not like their conceited ways and that they wer
not really so good as they thought they were. But Jesus too
a kinder way of opening their eyes to the foolishness of thei
pride. He told them a story about two men—a Pharisee wh
thought himself just about perfect and a tax collector wh
knew his own mistakes.

Before you read Jesus' story of the Pharisee and the ta
collector, listen to a true story about two men of our ow
day and our own country. Two men, who had never seer
each other before, stood on the shore looking at their boats
There were warnings over the radio that hurricane "Carol"
was heading their way, blowing with great fury.

One man had a cottage on the beach and a small motorboa
that he moored in a sheltered harbor. He did not pretend t
be much of a sailor. He worked in a city office most of th
time and came down to the shore only on vacations and week
ends.

The other man, a stranger on that beach, had sailed int
the harbor in a sleek big yacht. Obviously he did not wan
to be caught out in open water when "Carol" came whirlin

up the coast to whip the waves. He had tied his yacht beside a pier and was standing beside it looking out at the weather.

The man of the small boat was a friendly person. He did not boast that he knew much about boats or weather, but he did know what he had heard over the radio. And he was in the habit of being helpful. So he greeted the stranger politely and aid, "Are you sure that your yacht will be safe moored on hat side of the pier? After the eye of the hurricane passes, he wind will change. It could give your boat a vicious battering against the pier. I am quite familiar with the channels and the harbors around here. Can I help you find a safer mooring?"

What do you suppose the stranger answered? Never a word! He merely stared at the owner of the small boat with a haughty who-do-you-think-you-are expression. Then he turned and looked out over the sea again. The stranger waited till the owner of the small boat was out of sight before he unfastened his big yacht and sailed it up the river hunting for a safer place to ride out the storm.

After the yacht had gone, the man of the small boat learned hat the other man was a member of the Coast Guard.

"No wonder he scorned advice from an office worker like me!" he thought. "No wonder he thought he knew more than I do about the sea and the winds. How stupid of me to give advice to anyone who knows about boats and navigation and hurricanes!"

Two days later, however, when hurricane "Carol" had blown out its fury, the owner of the yacht was standing on he pier again. "Will you help me?" he asked the man of the small boat. "I thought I could sail out of the harbor mouth without using my chart. My yacht is stuck on a sand bar."

While the little boat was huffing and puffing to tow the big yacht off the sand bar, its owner was being most polite to the tranger. Not once did he say, "Perhaps you'll be willing to ask someone's advice next time!"

Afterward, when the man of the small boat told the story,

he was reminded of Jesus' story about the Pharisee and the tax collector, the story that Jesus told to "some who trusted in themselves that they were righteous and despised others." Read it in Luke 18:10-14.

The Whole Armor of God

EVEN WHEN HE WAS A BOY GROWING UP IN A SEAPORT CITY, PAUL saw plenty of Roman soldiers. With his eyes closed, he knew the sound of a soldier walking through the streets of Tarsus—clanking armor, clinking sword, and tramping shoes. Often he watched the sun glint on the polished metal of the helmet, belt, breast plate, shield, and sword of a soldier standing guard at a street corner or at the door of a public building. Perhaps the boy wondered if a soldier was just an ordinary Roman made brave by the armor which protected him. He knew that none of his Jewish relatives or neighbors dared stand against one of these armed soldiers. As a Jew himself, he felt no protection in his own long tunic and cloth turban. Perhaps the boy Paul thought that he, too, would dare swagger boldly through the streets if he were covered with heavy leather and strong metal, carrying a sword at his side.

When he became a man, Paul was even more familiar with the soldiers in armor. He saw them everywhere on his travels through the Roman Empire. Once he was rescued by soldiers when the Jewish mobs were beating him for teaching about Jesus Christ. More than once he was arrested by the Roman soldiers when the Jews complained about his teaching. He went through a long sea voyage from Palestine to Rome under the guard of a Roman soldier. The two were shipwrecked together. In Rome, although he was allowed to have his own rented house, he lived for two years with soldiers always keeping him a prisoner. He became friends with the soldiers of the palace guard and helped some of them learn about Christ. He had plenty of chance to become acquainted with these men and to realize that much of their courage and their strength came from their armor of leather and metal.

While he was kept prisoner by the soldiers in Rome, he had time to write wise letters to the young churches he had started in Greece and in Asia Minor. He wrote to encourage the new Christians to have faith that God would help them to follow Christ's way of love. He knew these men and women had learned only the first lessons about the Christian way. He feared they would have a hard time being brave when they were surrounded by men who made fun of their religion and urged them to go back to their old ways. He tried over and over in these letters to give his Christian friends courage to stand bravely in God's way.

One day Paul was writing the last words of a letter to friends at Ephesus. He wanted to tell them that God was their only hope in winning out against evil. He must say it in a way they would never forget. Perhaps, while he was pausing to think of just the right words to use, he heard the clank of the armor of the Roman soldier who was guarding him. Perhaps Paul remembered that it always seemed easier for the soldiers to be fearless because they were covered by metal and leather, and because they carried sharp swords in their scabbards. He must have thought to himself: "Christians have their own sort of armor. It is not made of heavy leather and shining metal. It is made of something even stronger. Anyone who has faith in God and tries to follow Christ's way can put on the whole armor of God."

Then Paul thought of the six parts of a soldier's armor: belt, breastplate, shoes, helmet, sword, and shield. And Paul thought of six kinds of strength that a Christian gets from God to fight the evil that surrounds him. These were truth, righteousness, good news of peace, salvation, the Word of God, and faith. Then Paul knew how he could finish his letter to his Christian friends in Ephesus. He used words that they could not forget and that the Christians who lived after them could never forget. He wrote:

> Be strong—not in yourselves but in the Lord. . . . You must wear the whole armor of God that you may be able to resist evil in its day of power, and that even when you have fought to a standstill you may still stand your ground. Take your stand with Truth as your belt, Righteousness your breastplate, the Gospel of Peace firmly on your feet, Salvation as your helmet, and in your hand the Sword of the Spirit, the Word of God. Above all be sure you take Faith as your shield, for it can quench every burning missile the enemy hurls at you. (Eph. 6:10, 13-17 Phillips.)

With armor like that—the whole armor of God—a Christian finds nothing too hard for him, whether he lived in the first century when Paul wrote his letters or whether he lives with us in the twentieth century.